INTRODUCTION

TO

LINEAR PROGRAMMING

SECOND EDITION

THE ALLYN AND BACON
SERIES IN QUANTITATIVE
METHODS FOR BUSINESS
AND ECONOMICS

R. STANSBURY STOCKTON
CONSULTING EDITOR

INTRODUCTION TO

ALLYN AND BACON, INC.

BOSTON

LINEAR PROGRAMMING

SECOND EDITION

R. STANSBURY STOCKTON

Professor and Chairman, Production Management Area,

Graduate School of Business

Indiana University

Library of Congress Catalog Card Number: 63-19120

Printed in the United States of America

First printing: May, 1963
Second printing: November, 1964
Third printing: August, 1965
Fourth printing: November, 1966

PREFACE

DURING THE THREE YEARS SINCE THE FIRST PUBLICATION OF THIS book linear programming has become an integral part of many courses in Schools of Business. The main issue now is not whether it should be taught but how much, where, and in what manner. Consequently, the objective of this edition, like the original, is to introduce students of business administration to linear programming methods.

The increasing mathematical competence of business students at both undergraduate and graduate levels has made it possible to raise our sights in many fields. Special courses and programs of study which stress the application of modern mathematics and statistics are no longer unusual. Such sources and programs are, however, appropriate only for a minority. The educational objective for most business students should be to develop a general administrative understanding of programming methods. *Introduction to Linear Programming* is designed to meet the need for suitable study materials to accomplish this limited objective.

Every effort has been made to explain programming methods in simple terms which are familiar to the business student. The ratio of words to symbols is somewhat higher than in most programming texts as a consequence. The desire to keep the text at the basic level has made it necessary to exclude many interesting aspects of linear programming. The student who wishes to develop special skills in the field will find the selected bibliography helpful in selecting advanced material in the field.

The descriptive material in Chapter 1 has been expanded in this edition so that the reader has a better understanding of the types of problems to which linear programming may be applied. The chapter on the transportation or distribution method has been rewritten and now includes Northwest Corner solutions, the MODI method, and methods for handling degenerate solutions. In addition, the number of exercises has been increased so that many new problems are included at the end of each chapter.

I am especially indebted to Professor Rocco Carzo of The Pennsylvania State University for his suggestions on the revision and to Mrs. Karen Strom who has typed most of the manuscript.

R. Stansbury Stockton

CONTENTS

1 ▸ LINEAR PROGRAMMING AND THE DECISION PROCESS[1]

1.1 THE MANAGER AND LINEAR PROGRAMMING

LINEAR PROGRAMMING is one of a number of recently developed analytical techniques that have proved useful in solving certain types of business problems. These quantitative methods of problem-solving, like many employed in operations research, are based upon mathematical and statistical concepts. Therefore, they present a problem to the business executive who finds it difficult to translate what appears to be mathematical "jibberish" into meaningful terms. Under such circumstances, the businessman tends to equate his inability to understand with impracticality and, as a consequence, to dismiss these new techniques as a plot by mathematicians to confuse and befuddle businessmen! There is evidently some truth in the adage that "People

[1] Much of the material in this chapter is drawn from the author's article "Linear Programming and Management," *Business Horizons,* Vol. 3, No. 2, Summer, 1960.

would rather live with problems which they cannot solve than with solutions to those problems which they cannot understand."

Publications in the field of management science contain an increasing number and variety of business applications of these analytical methods, including linear programming. Furthermore, the number and scope of these applications can be expected to increase in the future as variations and refinements in the methods are developed. The question is how they can be applied in a specific business.

Much of the credit for demonstrating the applicability of linear programming methods to business problems belongs to those people engaged in operations research. However, it is not necessary to be in operations research to learn the fundamentals of the subject. In fact, lack of understanding on the part of line managers appears to be a major factor limiting both present and future applications of many potentially useful explicit methods of analysis.

Inasmuch as linear programming represents a type of "model," one appropriate method of study would be to place it within the broader framework of the managerial decision-making process. Most statements of the latter are adaptations of the so-called scientific method. One of the justifications for the study of any quantitative method of analysis is that these methods illustrate all steps or phases of the decision-making process on an explicit basis. The assumption here is that the decision-making skills developed through the use of explicit exercises will be applicable to other problems, including those in which many factors are essentially qualitative.

A second reason for studying linear programming is that a general or "administrative" understanding of the method is a necessary prerequisite of effective use of the technique within any organization. Line managers — as differentiated from staff specialists or analysts — play an important role in the initial and final stages of problem-solving projects, that is, in the formulation of the problem and in the evaluation and application of the findings. They must, as a consequence, be capable of effective communication with any staff specialist, including the operations analyst. A more specific objective in the study of linear programming might, therefore, be stated as the development of sufficient insight into the method to enable one to (1) recognize problems that might be subjected to analysis by the method, (2) assist the analyst in the initial stage of the investigation, (3) evaluate and interpret the results intelligently, and (4) apply the results with the confidence that comes only with some understanding of the "whys" as well as the "whats" involved.

1.2 AREAS OF APPLICATION

Linear programming methods may chiefly be applied to the general class of problems known as *allocation problems*. Economists have traditionally defined such problems as those involving the allocation of scarce resources among alternative ends according to some criterion. Scarce resources for the business firm include capital, personnel, equipment, and materials. The various products and/or services that constitute the output of the firm represent alternative ends to which resources must be allocated. The criterion or objective, on the basis of which allocation decisions are to be made, may be some form of profit maximization or any other appropriate measure of desired performance.

Business managers always have been and always will be confronted with allocation decisions. The methods of analysis used to resolve these problems can and should be varied. For example, decisions based upon judgment and intuition may be satisfactory where the number of factors in the problem is limited and their relationships are clear. More difficult problems may require preliminary data collection, followed by the application of some formal method of analysis such as those characteristic of industrial engineering. The adequacy of these standard techniques falls off rapidly, however, as the number of variables in the problem increases. Linear programming is most appropriate for complex allocation problems that cannot be handled satisfactorily with conventional analytical techniques.

Many types of allocation problems are found in business,

especially in the production or operations function. Some examples to which linear programming methods have been successfully applied are:

Determination of product mix. The types and quantities of products to be manufactured during the next planning period must be determined. The relative profitability of the items in the product line varies. The planned product mix must take into consideration expected demand, the capability and capacities of production and distribution facilities, and management policies, such as policy on products carried to "round out the line." Given these limitations or restrictions on the mix, the solution should also make maximum economic sense; that is, it should maximize profits.

Blending or mixing problems. One or more products are manufactured by mixing or blending various ingredients; for example, paint, cattle feed, petroleum products. Many different combinations of these ingredients can result in end products that will meet all technical specifications. Given the availability and relative costs of the ingredients, which blend will result in minimum material cost per unit of end product?

Production scheduling and inventory planning. Given a seasonal demand and limited production facilities, what production schedule and planned inventory levels over the next planning period will meet expected demand and also result in minimum cost?

Machine loading. A series of orders is to be processed through a group of machines. The cost of processing each order depends in part on the particular machine to which it is assigned. Limited machine capacity precludes assignment of each order to the lowest-cost equipment. What allocations of available capacity to the series of orders will result in minimum total processing cost?

Shipping and physical distribution problems. Goods are to be shipped from several production facilities having limited capacities to field warehouses that anticipate a given demand over the next planning period. Transportation and/or production costs vary among the alternative methods of supplying the warehouses. What physical distribution pattern will be both within the capacity and demand restrictions and will at the same time minimize total production and distribution costs over the planning period?

1.3 BASIC ASSUMPTIONS

All explicit analytical methods are based upon certain assumptions. Just as one must understand certain accounting conventions to use accounting statements intelligently, one must understand the basic assumption of any quantitative analytical tool if it is to be applied properly. The two central assumptions in all linear programming methods are (1) *linearity,* and (2) *certainty. Linearity* means that all problem relationships can be expressed in the form of linear equations. The straight-line method of depreciation assumes that capital value decreases at a linear rate. Break-even charts assume that both variable costs and revenue are linear functions; that is, that they increase in direct proportion to output. The term *certainty* indicates that no significant variations are expected in the numerical value for a problem factor. Average cost, for example, may be used in making a decision even though actual cost may vary slightly from this average. Statistical quality control, on the other hand, is based upon the expected variations in a process within the control limits, i.e., a degree of uncertainty exists. Linear programming is an appropriate analytical tool only for those complex allocation problems that are characterized by both linearity and certainty.

An understanding of linear functions is so fundamental to understanding linear programming that Chapter 2 is devoted to a general review of this subject. The exact meaning and significance of linearity and certainty in a programming context will become apparent in the explanations of the various methods. It should be noted that, by reducing the mathematical complexity of the methods, these assumptions make linear programming a good starting point for the beginning student of quantitative methods of analysis. The ultimate payoff, of course, is in solving real problems. The usefulness of linear programming, like any other method of analysis, is dependent in large part on the reasonableness of the assumptions about the problem being studied.

1.4 LINEAR PROGRAMMING METHODS

The mathematical computational procedures of linear programming depend in part on which of the several programming methods is adopted for a particular problem. The basic or general case is called the *Simplex* method, since it is based upon the simplex algorithm. Certain types of allocation problems may be solved by special, less complex, versions of the Simplex method known as the Graphical and Transportation methods. In addition, there are a number of variations such as the so-called Index method, which yields only approximate solutions but has minimum computational requirements. All methods are, in effect, nothing more than effective search procedures that seek optimal solutions to allocation problems in which there are more unknowns than linear equations. In this sense, linear programming may be viewed as systematic trial and error in which the most promising shortcuts to a solution are indicated by mathematics rather than intuition and elbow grease.

1.5 COMPUTERS AND LINEAR PROGRAMMING

Formulating a business problem for solution by any linear programming method requires setting up a large number of linear equations. Once the problem is framed, an initial solution is determined. A set of operating rules is then applied to determine if a better solution exists and, if so, to develop an improved solution. The solution process is iterative; that is, the rules are applied again and again until such time as an optimal solution is found.

1.5 COMPUTERS AND LINEAR PROGRAMMING

The fact that the computational rules and procedures for linear programming are so well defined makes this a natural application for modern electronic computers. Standard programs are available for linear programming on nearly all computer hardware today so that the burdensome task of computer programming is less of an obstacle than in earlier years. Problems of limited complexity, like those included in subsequent chapters, may be solved efficiently on paper. However, as the number of variables in the problem increases, the magnitude of the computational task increases sharply. For this reason the use of expensive computer time can be justified in the analysis of most complex business problems.

2 ▸ LINEARITY AND LINEAR EQUATIONS

2.1 LINEARITY AND PROBLEM-SOLVING

THE CONCEPT of linearity is an abstraction that is frequently used in the analysis of certain problems found in life. Many personal decisions involve the assumption of linear relationships even though we may not be conscious of these assumptions. From a practical standpoint, as long as decisions made on the basis of an informal, intuitive, and highly personalized analysis "work," there is little to be gained by questioning the assumptions. In business, however, problem-solving often requires formal methods of analysis. Many individuals may be involved both in the analysis of the problem and in the application of the results. Where this is the case, it is important that assumptions concerning the relationships between factors in the problem be made explicit.

Inasmuch as linearity is one of the basic assumptions, a general knowledge of the concept is useful to the student of business. One should keep in mind, however, that the concept of linearity has many applications above and beyond those found in linear programming.

2.2 SYMBOLIC EXPRESSIONS FOR RELATIONSHIPS BETWEEN VARIABLES

Suppose that observation of certain phenomena convinces one that there is some relationship between factors X and Y. One method of expressing this relationship would be to describe it with words, that is, with a verbal model. For example, "it appears that the value of Y generally depends upon the value of X." Provided that a very general statement of this type is sufficient, words are an acceptable tool to use in describing the relationship between the variables. However, as the number of variables increases and their inter-relationships become more complex, words become cumbersome and inadequate tools for model-building. Fortunately, this is a problem that mathematicians and statisticians solved long ago. The use of symbolic expressions is a second and more precise method for expressing relationships. Thus, the mathematician would simply write: $Y = F(X)$. These statements may be read as "the value of Y is a function of (depends on) the value of X" or more simply as "Y is a function of X." By convention, X is called the independent variable and Y the dependent variable, since the value of the latter depends on the value of the former.

Although the expression $Y = F(X)$ represents a notational improvement over the verbal description, it remains very general in the sense that we still do not know the exact nature of the relationship between the two variables. In solving business problems, for example, it is not too helpful to know only that "profits depend on sales."

2.3 MEANING OF LINEARITY

Linearity represents a special case of the relationship $Y = F(X)$. The relationship may be defined as linear if, for all possible values of X and Y, a given change in the value of X produces a constant change in the value of Y.

2.31 Nongraphical Interpretation. Consider the table of values given below:

TABLE 2.1

X	Change in X	Y	Change in Y
−3		−7	
−2	+1	−4	+3
−1	+1	−1	+3
0	+1	2	+3
1	+1	5	+3
2	+1	8	+3
3	+1	11	+3

In this example, $Y = F(X)$ is linear since a given change in X (always + 1) produces a constant change in the value of Y (always + 3).

Now consider this second table:

TABLE 2.2

X	Change in X	Y	Change in Y
0		0	
1	+1	1	+1
2	+1	4	+3
3	+1	9	+5
4	+1	16	+7

This relationship between X and Y is nonlinear, since the change in X (always + 1) produces varying changes in Y.

2.32 Graphical Interpretation. Plotting the data from Table 2.1 on a graph (Figure 2.1) reveals that all of the points lie on a straight line. The graph of a linear equation is always a straight line. The points of Table 2.2 form a curve rather than a straight line, thus indicating that it is a nonlinear relationship.

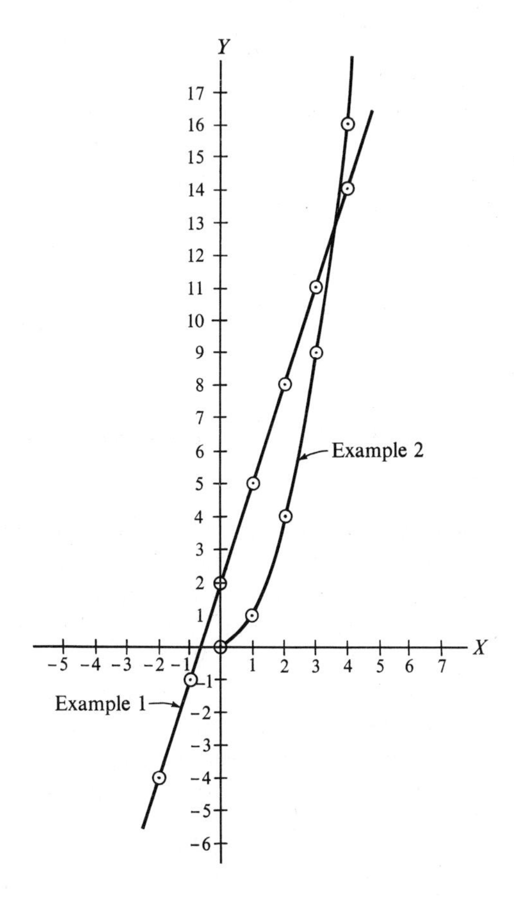

Figure 2.1

2.4 LINEAR EQUATIONS

The general expression of a linear function of one independent variable (slope intercept form) is $F(X) = a + b(X)$, usually written $Y = a + b(X)$ or $Y = a + bX$, where:

Y is the dependent variable
X is the independent variable
a is a numerical constant called the *intercept*
b is a numerical constant called the *slope*

The intercept (a) is the point where the line crosses the Y axis, that is, it is the value for Y when X is zero. In Table 2.1 this occurred at 2, that is, $a = 2$. The slope (b) of a linear function (straight line) is the amount of change in Y caused by a unit (1) change in X. In Table 2.1 each unit change in X produced a change of $+ 3$ in the value for Y; thus, $b = 3$. The equation of the function described in Table 2.1 is, therefore, $Y = 2 + 3\ (X)$ or $Y = 2 + 3X$.

2.5 DETERMINATION OF THE EQUATION OF A LINE

Occasionally it is necessary to find the equation of a line based upon limited information. This can be done provided that the coordinates are known for at least two points on the line. For example, suppose that at point 1, $X = X_1$ and $Y = Y_1$, and that, at point 2, $X = X_2$ and $Y = Y_2$ (where X_1, X_2, Y_1, and Y_2 are specific values for X and Y). The change in Y from point 1 to point 2 would be $(Y_2 - Y_1)$ and the change in X between in Y by the total change in X between the points would give us the change in Y per unit change in X, that is, the slope of the line,

$$b = \frac{Y_2 - Y_1}{X_2 - X_1} \qquad (2.1)$$

EXAMPLE. Suppose that the following points are known for a linear function:

At point 1, $X_1 = 1$ and $Y_1 = 5$
At point 2, $X_2 = 3$ and $Y_2 = 11$

Using Eq. (2-1),

$$b = \frac{Y_2 - Y_1}{X_2 - X_1} = \frac{11 - 5}{3 - 1} = \frac{6}{2} = \frac{3}{1} = 3$$

The general equation for a line is $Y = a + b(X)$. Since the specific value for (b) is now known, the expression for this particular function may now be written as $Y = a + 3(X)$ or $Y = a + 3X$.

To find the value of the intercept (a), substitute the values for X and Y at one of the known points. For example, using point 1, where $X_1 = 1$ and $Y_1 = 5$,

$$Y = a + 3(X)$$
$$5 = a + 3(1)$$
$$a = 2$$

The complete expression may now be written at
$Y = 2 + 3(X)$.

2.6 DETERMINATION OF INTERCEPTS

In business one is frequently confronted with the problem of evaluating alternative courses of action, and interest frequently centers on the special case where the consequences of two or more alternatives are equal.

2.61 Graphical Determination of Intercepts. Consider the following linear equations, which have been plotted in Figure 2.2:

$$Y_1 = 2 + X_1 \tag{2.2}$$
$$Y_2 = 2\,X_2 \tag{2.3}$$
$$Y_3 = 10 - \tfrac{1}{2}\,X_3 \tag{2.4}$$

Note that Eq. (2.4) has a negative slope; that is, the value of Y decreases as the value of X increases. This is the type of line most frequently encountered in the graphical method.

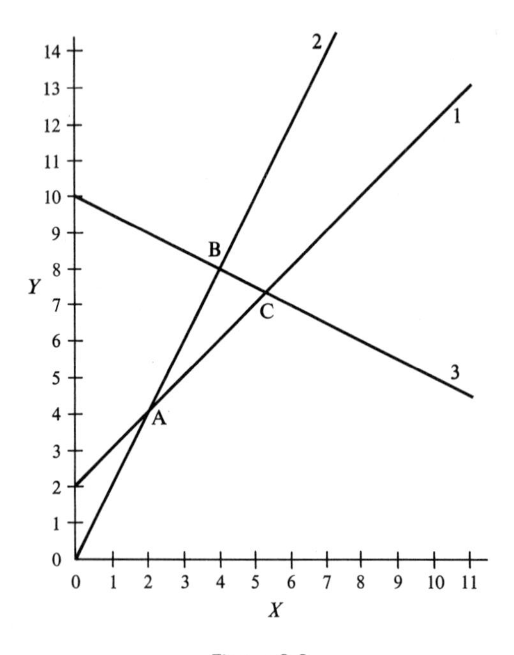

Figure 2.2

It is evident from the graph that the Y values for Eqs. (lines) (2.2) and (2.3) are equal ($Y_1 = Y_2 = 4$) when X_1 and X_2 are both equal to 2. Similarly, Eqs. (2.3) and (2.4) "cross" at $X = 4$ and $Y = 8$. The intersection of Eqs. (2.2) and (2.4) is somewhat more difficult to determine precisely. Perhaps the best answer that could be given at this point is that their point of intersection is somewhere between an X value of 5 and 6 and a Y value of 7 and 8. Graphs typically do not produce precise results. If more accurate answers are required, one must resort to other methods of analysis.

2.62 Algebraic Solution for Intercepts. When two lines "cross" one another, this means that at that particular point (X value) the Y values are equal. At all other X values, of course, the corresponding Y values would be different. If we are interested only in the point of intersection (crossover), we can take advantage of this temporary equality.

At point A:

$$Y_1 = 2 + X$$
$$Y_2 = 2X$$

But we also know $Y_1 = Y_2$ (at this special point only). Substitution gives us:

$$\begin{aligned} Y_1 &= Y_2 \\ 2 + X &= 2X \\ 2 &= 2X - X \\ 2 &= X \qquad \text{(value of } X_1 \text{ and } X_2 \text{ at intersection)} \end{aligned}$$

The value of Y that results from a value of $X = 2$ in both equations is:

$$\begin{aligned} Y_1 &= 2 + X \\ &= 2 + 2 \\ &= 4 \end{aligned} \qquad \begin{aligned} Y_2 &= 2(X) \\ &= 2(2) \\ &= 4 \end{aligned}$$

At point B:

$$\left.\begin{aligned} Y_2 &= Y_3 \\ 2X &= 10 - \tfrac{1}{2}X \\ 2X + \frac{X}{2} &= 10 \\ \frac{5}{2}X &= 10 \\ X &= 4 \end{aligned}\right\} \text{Thus:} \qquad \begin{aligned} Y_2 &= 2X \\ &= 2\ (4) \\ &= 8 \\ Y_3 &= 10 - \frac{X}{2} \\ &= 10 - \frac{4}{2} \\ &= 8 \end{aligned}$$

Develop your own solution for point C (the proper values are $X = 5\ 1/3$ and $Y = 7\ 1/3$).

2.7 EXERCISES

1. The following values for X and Y are given:

X	Y
9	60
10	57
11	54
12	51
15	42

   a. Is this a linear function? Why or why not?
   b. What equation describes this relationship?
   c. Determine the X and Y intercepts.

2. Three linear equations are given as follows:

$$Y = 46 - \frac{4}{5}X$$
$$Y = \frac{3}{2}X$$
$$Y = 7 + \frac{1}{2}X$$

   a. Plot these equations on graph paper. Approximate their intercepts from your plot.
   b. Determine the three intercepts directly from the equations; that is, give an algebraic solution.

3. Mr. John Franklin is a salesman who drives his own car on company business. His employer reimburses him for such travel at the rate of 9 cents per mile. Franklin estimates that his fixed costs per year, such as taxes, insurance, and depreciation, are \$513. The direct or variable costs, such as gas, oil, and lubrication, average about 3.6 cents per mile.

   a. Draw a break-even chart (total annual cost *vs.* miles) and determine the number of miles Franklin must drive each year on company business to break even on total automobile expenses.
   b. Determine his break-even point algebraically by finding the point of intersection for the equations that describe his "in-

come" from driving the automobile and his total annual expense of owning and operating the automobile.

4. The Saveio Company is anticipating an order for a machined part. The size of the order has not yet been specified by the customer. Three manufacturing alternatives exist for producing this part. Method No. 1 will involve tooling costs of $180 and a direct cost per unit of $2.50. Method No. 2 involves more extensive tooling, having a cost of $390, but would reduce direct cost to $1.30 per unit. Method No. 3 involves no tooling and utilizes direct labor only. The expected cost per unit using this alternative would be $3.90.
   a. Determine the total cost per order and the cost per unit for each of the methods using the following order sizes: 60, 120, 200, 300.
   b. Plot the total costs obtained from (a) on a graph. Determine from your graph the approximate order sizes at which the costs for the alternatives are equal.
   c. Write a linear equation which describes the total cost per order for each manufacturing method. Use these equations to determine the exact order size at which total cost is equal.
   d. What advantage does the use of equations in the analysis of this problem have over the tabular approach used in (a) above? Explain.

3 ▸ THE GRAPHICAL METHOD

THE GRAPHICAL method of linear programming is limited in application to certain types of elementary problems. Most business problems worth subjecting to formal analysis within a linear programming format would probably be far too complex for the graphical method. It is, however, the simplest method and as such is a useful starting point in any discussion of linear programming fundamentals.

3.1 PROCEDURE

It is essential that a logical and systematic procedure be used for problem-solving so that maximum results may be accomplished with minimum expenditures of time and effort. The suggested procedure for the graphical method is as follows:

1. Frame the problem.
   a. Determine the restrictions or constraints.
      (1) Make numerical computations required. (Only two points need to be determined for linear restrictions.

(2) Determine polygon of technical feasibility through graphical display of linear restrictions.

b. Select an appropriate objective function.

(1) Measure of effectiveness should be consistent with higher order objectives.

(2) The function must be linear.

2. Solve for the optimum solution, using either:

a. Direct graphical method.

b. Algebraic method using basic solutions.

3. Modify the solution to take account of those factors in the problem that are not included in the quantitative portion of the analysis.[1]

The meaning and significance of this procedure are best demonstrated by example. The remainder of this chapter will, therefore, be devoted to a sample problem.

THE BAKER'S DECISION

The owner of a small bakery that specializes in cookies is concerned with the kinds and quantities of cookies to be prepared for sale tomorrow. Let us assume that there are only two kinds of cookies — sugar cookies and iced cookies — from which he may select his offering to the buying public.

3.2 TECHNICAL PHASES OF THE PROBLEM (DETERMINATION OF RESTRICTIONS)

Like any production system, the bakery has limited resources available to create end products. Since we are concerned with what to produce tomorrow, the bakery's resources are relatively fixed. There is little opportunity, for example, to in-

[1] Technically, this is not part of the procedure for linear programming. It is included here to emphasize the decision-making approach.

crease overnight either the size of the work force or the equipment available. As a consequence, the baker's short-run capability to produce is restricted by the amount of material, labor, equipment, and other resources available to him during the period of time over which the decision will be effective. Any product-mix decision made by the bakery manager must, therefore, be technically or physically feasible, in the sense that it is possible to accomplish the task with the available resources.

Let us assume that the following production resources are available:

Cookie mix — 120 pounds
Icing mix — 32 pounds
Baking equipment — continuous oven with capacity of 120 dozen per day
Bakery labor — 15 hours.

In order to analyze the problem, we need to know exactly what "scarce resources" are required to produce the alternative products or "ends." The recipes provide this information. For example, one dozen iced cookies require 1.0 pounds of cookie mix and 0.4 pounds of icing mix. One dozen sugar cookies consume 0.6 pounds of cookie mix and no icing mix.[2] Through experience the baker knows that 0.10 hours of bakery labor are required per dozen sugar cookies. The same requirement for iced cookies is 0.15 per dozen.[3]

3.21 Determination of Cookie Mix Restriction. At this point we can begin to limit the number of alternatives available to the decision-maker. For example, should he elect to produce only sugar cookies, he has enough cookie mix on hand to produce only 200 dozen (120 ÷ 0.6). In view of his limited cookie mix resource, any decision to produce more than that quantity of sugar cookies is not a technically feasible alternative. Similarly, it is not technically feasible to produce more than 120 dozen

[2] Note the similarity of the recipe to the bill of material and operations sheet in metal-working plants.

[3] Note that all data for the problem are given as exact numbers rather than as probability distributions. Certainty is assumed.

iced cookies (120 ÷ 1.0) if only iced cookies are produced. These two figures, then, represent the maximum possible production of each product if produced exclusively. It is also possible, of course, to produce many combinations of these two products. Only those combinations that require a total of 120 pounds or less of cookie mix are, however, technically feasible. Several potential combinations are shown in Table 3.1.

TABLE 3.1

	Dozens		Cookie Mix		
Combination	Sugar	Iced	Sugar	Iced	Total
1	200	0	120 pounds	0 pounds	120 pounds
2	150	30	90 "	30 "	120 "
3	100	60	60 "	60 "	120 "
4	50	90	30 "	90 "	120 "
5	0	120	0 "	120 "	120 "

It is apparent that for every 50 dozen sugar cookies the baker "gives up" in his product mix, enough cookie mix is "released" to produce 30 dozen iced cookies. This is not surprising, since the ratio of this ingredient in the two products is 3 to 5 (0.6 to 1.0). Another way of stating this relationship is that the *exchange rate* or physical rate of substitution of these two products in terms of a particular mutually required resource is 3 to 5.

Suppose, now, that we relate the information developed about the availability of cookie mix as a constraint on the decision and the rate of substitution between sugar and iced cookies relative to this constraint, and display it on a graph. The five points from Table 3.1 are shown in Figure 3.1.

These points all fall on the line determined by the two "exclusive maximums" ($Q_S = 0$, $Q_I = 120$) and (200, 0) determined earlier. Thus, if these two intercepts can be determined and rate of substitution remains constant, the restriction line can be drawn between them.[4] This restriction or constraint is simply a graphical display of the ways in which the cookie mix resource could be allocated. Thus, any of the following combinations are feasible (50, 60) (100, 50) (150, 25) because they lie between the origin and the restriction and would consume less than 120 pounds of cookie mix.[5] Points that fall outside the shaded area (50, 120) (100, 90) (150, 60) are not feasible decisions in terms of the mix available for tomorrow's production.

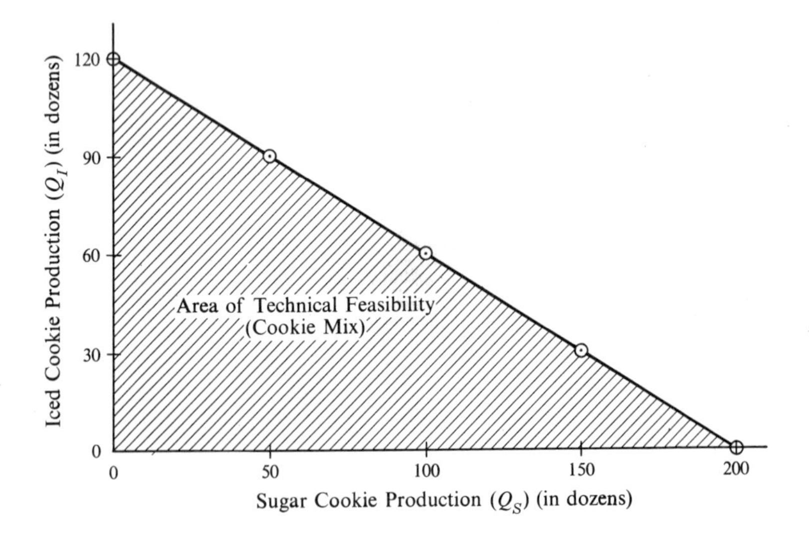

Figure 3.1

[4] If the rate of substitution were not constant, the constraint would not be a linear one. This would not fit one of the basic assumptions of linear programming.

[5] The equation of the line is $Q_I = 120 - \frac{0.6}{1} Q_S = 120 - \frac{3}{5} Q_S$

Note that the coefficient of the last term represents the rate of substitution and is, therefore, the slope of the line.

3.22 Determination of Additional Restrictions. We are now ready to determine the additional technical constraints on the decision. The 15 direct labor hours available, for example, might be allocated to the production of 100 dozen iced cookies (15 ÷ 0.15), 150 dozen sugar cookies (15 ÷ 0.1), or any combination of the two that requires 15 or less direct labor hours. A plot of this information on the graph (Figure 3.2) indicates that this constraint is more restrictive than that for cookie mix.[6] As

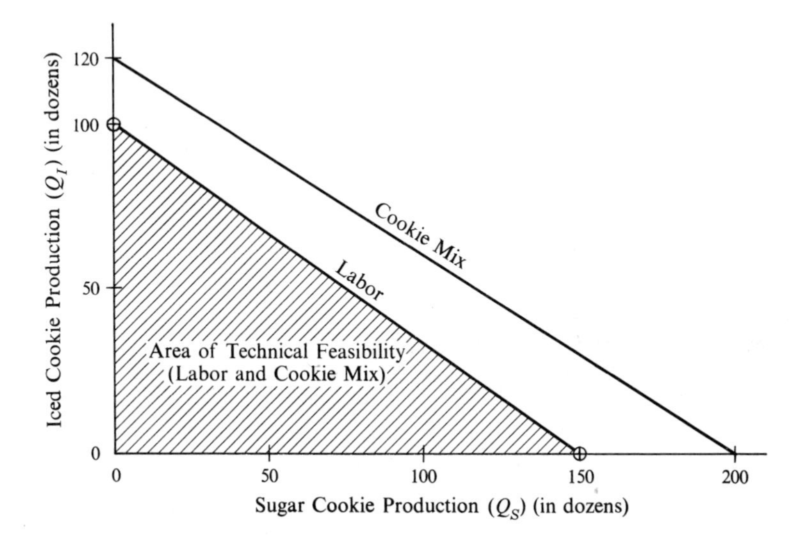

Figure 3.2

a consequence, the area of technical feasibility, in terms of both cookie mix and direct labor, becomes the area defined by the latter resource alone. Expressed another way, the baker has more than enough cookie mix to make any of the possible com-

[6] The equation of the direct labor constraint is

$$Q_I = 100 - \frac{.1}{.15} Q_S = 100 - \frac{2}{3} Q_S$$

The rate of substitution is 2 to 3 for the labor resource.

binations permitted by the scarce resource, direct labor. For this reason, we can ignore the cookie mix in our further analysis; it is not a strategic or key technical factor in this particular problem. If, however, the baker were concerned with deciding how much cookie mix to order tomorrow — a different problem — the amount of cookie mix on hand would obviously be an important factor.

3.23 The Technical Feasibility Polygon. Figure 3.3 shows the effect of all technical constraints on the problem. Note that icing

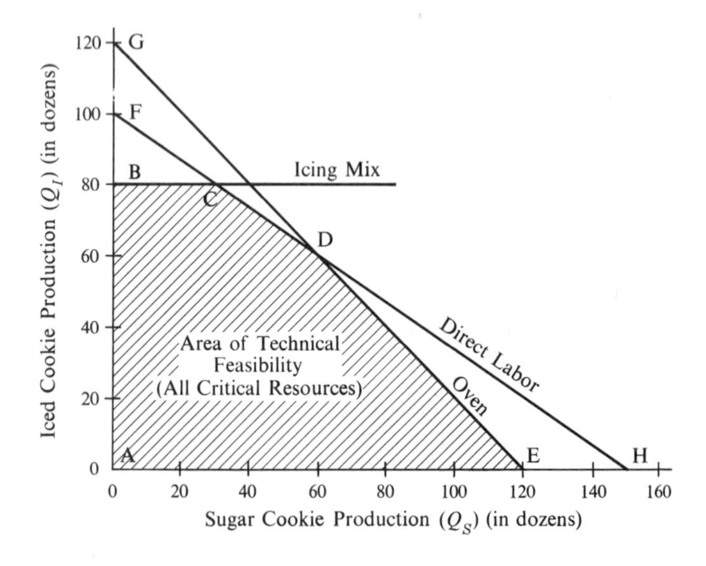

Figure 3.3

mix is a constraint on the production of iced cookies only. There is no rate of substitution between the two product ends relative to this specialized resource. Giving up the production of some iced cookies, for example, in order to free some of the icing mix resource for the production of sugar cookies has no practical technical meaning, since the latter do not utilize this resource. On the other hand, the rate of substitution for the ovens is one to one: the ovens can produce one dozen sugar cookies for every dozen iced cookies given up, and vice versa.

The net effect of technical constraints is to limit the number of alternative solutions available to the decision maker. The baker, however, still has a very large number of alternatives from which he must choose. Any combination within the area of the technical feasibility polygon is a physically feasible decision for tomorrow's product mix.

Having thus determined the effect of the physical factors in the problem, we can now examine the economic phases of the problem.

3.3 ECONOMIC PHASES OF THE PROBLEM

One of the decisions that must be made in the so-called observation stage of the scientific method is to determine an objective function, or measure of effectiveness. Since a bakery is an economic institution, it would be reasonable to assume that the highest order economic objective of the firm would be maximization of return on investment. Figure 3.4 indicates the first few stages of the approach to this objective.

Let us assume that (1) all of the technically feasible alternatives (product quantities) are realistic from the standpoint of a sales forecast, and (2) investment is fixed in the short run, that is, no changes in total investment can be made for tomorrow.[7] The objective, then, might be restated as maximizing the total dollar contribution to fixed costs (overhead expenses) and profit.[8]

Suppose that the selling price per dozen iced cookies is 70¢ and the direct material and labor costs associated with their production is 50¢ per dozen; the corresponding data for plain sugar cookies might be 60¢ and 45¢ respectively. Every dozen iced

[7] If any of the feasible production quantities exceed the sales forecast, one might use the expected sales quantities as additional constraints on the decision.

[8] From Figure 3.4.

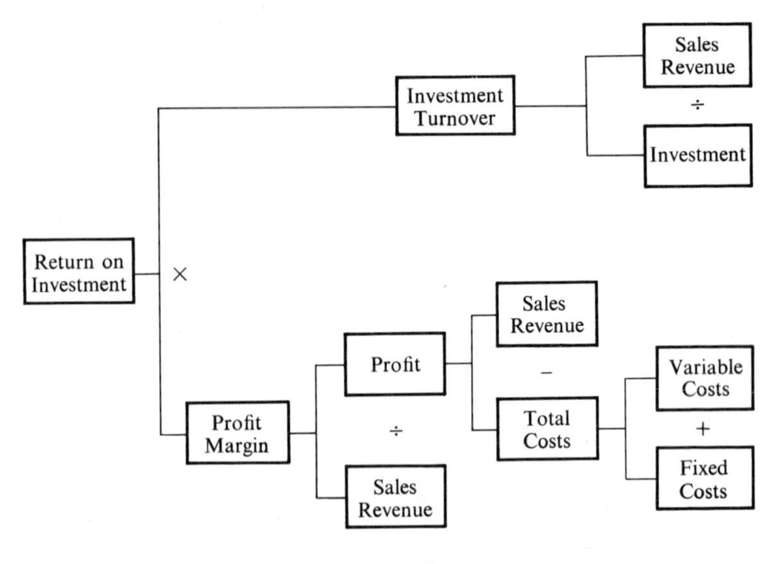

Figure 3.4

cookies sold "contributes" 20¢ to fixed costs (at all quantities below the break-even point) or to profit (for all output over the break-even point). In like manner, the "contribution" of sugar cookies is 15¢ per dozen. Knowing this, our bakery manager can now proceed to determine the most economically desirable of the many feasible alternatives. This is the *optimal* economic solution.

It would be useful at this point to state the objective function in terms that will allow explicit evaluation of various solutions that may be indicated. The objective is to maximize the total dollar contribution to overhead and profit. This can be expressed in symbolic form as follows:

Return on Investment:

= Investment Turnover times Profit Margin or $IT \times PM$.

$$= \frac{SR}{I} \times \frac{P}{SR} = \frac{(SR - TC)}{I} = \frac{SR - (VC + FC)}{I}$$

$$= \frac{(SR - VC) - FC}{I}$$

If costs and investment are fixed in the short run, then maximizing total dollar contribution (sales revenue minus variable costs) becomes the short-run equivalent of maximizing return on investment.

$$TC = Q_I \times C_I + Q_S \times C_S \tag{3.1}$$

where:

TC = Total dollar contribution

Q_I = Production of iced cookies (dozens)

C_I = Contribution of iced cookies (per dozen)

Q_S = Production of sugar cookies (dozens)

C_S = Contribution of sugar cookies (per dozen)

3.4 DETERMINATION OF THE OPTIMAL SOLUTION

In framing the problem we have developed one equation and two independent variables (Q_S and Q_I). This complicates the solution process because there are a very large number of values for Q_S and Q_I that will "satisfy" the single equation. All of the combinations in Table 3.2, for example, produce a total contribution of $6.00.

TABLE 3.2

	Production		Contribution		
Mix	Iced	Sugar	Iced	Sugar	Total
1	30	0	$6.00	$0.00	$6.00
2	24	8	4.80	1.20	6.00
3	18	16	3.60	2.40	6.00
4	6	32	1.20	4.80	6.00
5	0	40	0.00	6.00	6.00

These are "solutions" for the equation, but not for the problem. We are interested in finding those values for Q_S and Q_I that (1) maximize the objective function (total dollar contribution in this case) and (2) remain within the technical restrictions imposed by the limited resources.

One method of determining the optimal solution would be trial and error. By inserting different values for the quantity of sugar and iced cookies to be produced in Eq. (3.1), we might eventually find those values that represent the optimal production program. An alternative would be to use one of the solution methods characteristic of the graphical method of linear programming. These two methods make it possible to determine the optimal solution with the least possible computation. Linear programming may, in fact, be described as an effective search procedure for determining optimal solutions to types of problems in which there are more unknowns than linear equations.

Before proceeding with the specifics of these solution methods, it might be interesting to attempt an intuitive decision. We might reason, for example, that since the contribution of one product is higher than that of the other, an optimal solution would be (1) to produce as many iced cookies as possible, and (2) to use any resources not required for the production of iced cookies to produce sugar cookies. Such a decision makes sense, but does it make maximum sense? The graphical methods described in the following pages should provide us with a basis for evaluation of this intuitive decision rule.

3.41 Direct Graphical Solution. If the values of Table 3.2 are plotted on a graph (Figure 3.5), they trace a straight line of the equation, $Y = 30 - \frac{3}{4}(X)$. This is not surprising, since Eq. (3.1) is a linear function. Furthermore, the slope of the line is the ratio of contributions for the products ($.15 \div .20 = \frac{3}{4}$). Any point on this line, then, represents a solution that is feasible and results in a total contribution of $6.00. Our objective, however, is to maximize the total contribution, so these do not appear to be optimal solutions.

In Figure 3.6, the lines of "equal contribution" have been drawn in for $12.00, $18.00 and $21.00. Notice that the

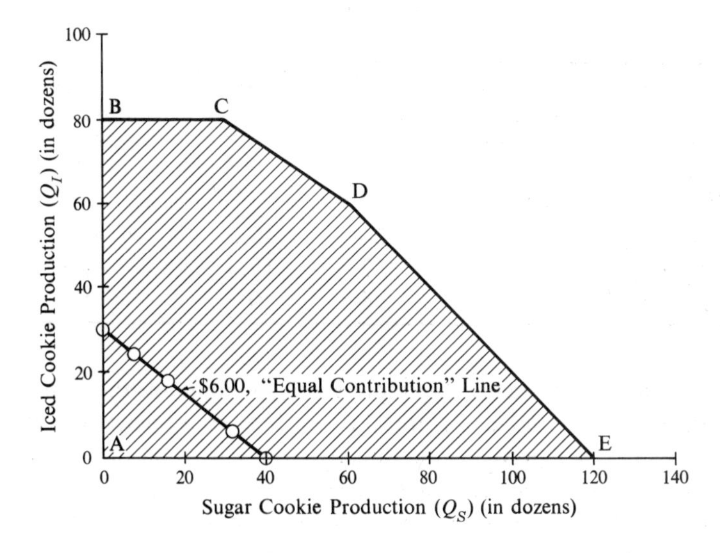

Figure 3.5

"equal contribution" lines are parallel since their slopes are equal. It is necessary to use a dashed line for a portion of the $18.00 line since some of those combinations represent solutions that are not technically feasible. Were we to continue drawing parallel lines further out from the origin, the solutions outside the area of technical feasibility would increase. Finally, one line would just intersect point *D* (see $21.00 line). The optimal solution indicated at this point is 60 dozen each of the sugar and iced cookies; the corresponding profit is $21.00. We also know that both the direct labor and oven capacity will be fully utilized while there will be extra capacity (slack) in terms of the other resources — icing and cookie mixes. Table 3.3 gives this information in tabular form.

3.42 Algebraic Solution. A second and more direct method of solving graphical linear programming problems is to work exclusively with those solutions represented by the points on the polygon of technical feasibility. As might be expected, the optimal

TABLE 3.3

	Cookie Mix (pounds)	Icing Mix (pounds)	Labor (hours)	Oven (dozen per day)
Sugar	36	0	6.0	60
Iced	60	24	9.0	60
Total	96	24	15.0	120
Capacity	120	32	15.0	120
"Slack"	24	8	0	0

solution will normally be represented by one of these points (*B*, *C*, *D*, or *E* in Figure 3.6).[9] The coordinates of these points may be approximated directly from the graph or computed algebraically using the equations for the various constraints and the method suggested in Sec. 2.6 for determining the point of intersection for two linear functions. These coordinates are shown in Table 3.4.

TABLE 3.4

Point	Iced	Sugar
A	0 dozen	0 dozen
B	80 "	0 "
C	80 "	30 "
D	60 "	60 "
E	0 "	120 "

The analysis may conveniently be started at the origin solution (point *A* in Figure 3.6).[10] This is a technically feasible solution even though it makes no economic sense. Total contribution Eq. (3.1) would be equal to zero. The intuitive de-

[9] In the special case when the slope of the "equal contribution" lines is the same as that of one of the constraints, there will be a range of optimal solutions.

[10] The reason for starting at the origin will become more apparent when the simplex method is introduced.

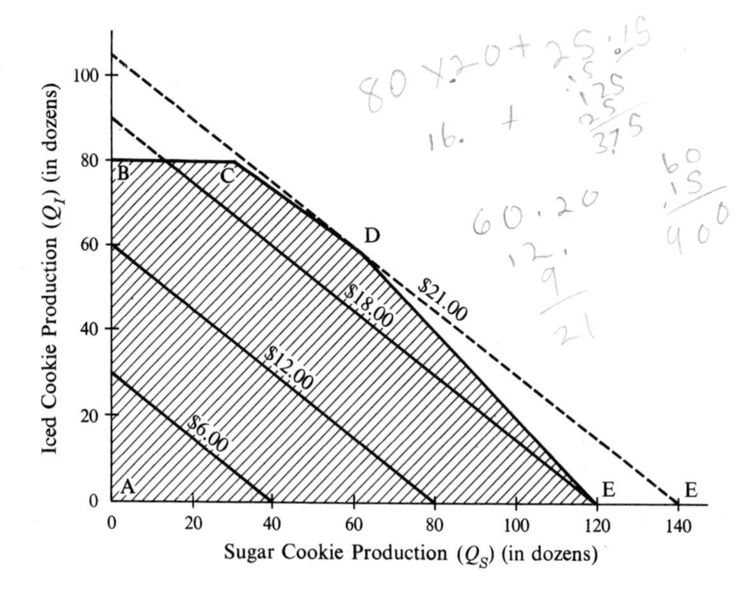

Figure 3.6

cision rule developed in Sec. 3.4 would indicate that as many dozens of iced cookies as possible should now be introduced into the solution. The visual analogy would be to move from point *A* to point *B* (Figure 3.6). The value of the objective function at this point would be \$16.00 (80 × .20 + 0 × .15). This would require all of the icing mix resource, but a substantial amount of slack, or unused capacity, would remain for labor and the ovens. Our intuitive rule would indicate, therefore, that we begin to introduce quantities of the next most profitable product into the solution, that is, we move in the direction of point C. Each dozen of sugar cookies adds 15¢ to the objective function. At point *C*, however, we encounter the direct labor constraint. This presumably represents the optimal solution by our intuitive evaluation, inasmuch as we are maximizing production of our most profitable product and are producing as much as possible of the second most profitable product with the remaining capacity. Total dollar contribution at point *C* is 80 × .20 + 30 × .15 = \$20.50. It is known from the direct graphical analysis (Sec. 3.41) that this is not the true optimal solution. Why did the intuitive answer fail?

The answer to this question lies in the relative rates of substitution and profitability in the problem. Moving from point *C* to point *D* on the graph implies that the baker "trades" units of labor capacity between the products. Since iced cookies require .15 labor hours per dozen and sugar cookies require only .1 hours per dozen, each dozen iced cookies may be "traded" for one and one-half dozen sugar cookies. This makes technical sense, but what about the economic sense? A dozen iced cookies contribute 20¢, but 1½ dozen sugar cookies contribute 22.5¢ (15 × 1.5). Changing the product mix from point *C* to *D* is, therefore, a profitable move, as shown below:

Value of objective function at point *C*		$20.50
Added contribution from sugar cookies (30 dozen @ 15¢)	$4.50	
Loss of contribution — iced cookies (20 dozen @ 20¢)	$4.00	
Net added contribution	.50	
Value of objective function at point *D*		$21.00

Would it also be profitable to move from point *D* to *E*, to give up oven capacity for iced cookies in order to produce more sugar cookies? The rate of substitution for the oven resource is one to one. Such a change would result in a 5¢ decrease (20¢ – 15¢) in the value of the objective function for each dozen "traded off" in the solution. Therefore, point D represents the optimum economic solution to our problem as given.[11]

[11] It is also possible to solve the problem by introducing the maximum number of sugar cookies into the solution first. As long as desirable "trades" can be made (as measured by the objective function) the solution is being improved. In more complex problems the number of trials required to reach the optimum solution is ordinarily reduced by introducing the products in order of their desirability at each stage. Desirability has, in effect, been defined in this case as contribution per dozen. Other definitions may be more appropriate, as will be illustrated in Chapter 4.

Before reaching an economic conclusion, the baker should review and re-evaluate two factors. One is the realism of the assumptions made thus far in his analysis. Are all of the relationships really linear? If not, is the assumption of linearity so severe an abstraction as to negate the results of the analysis? A second factor is the treatment of the data employed. Are they really certainties or only probabilities?[12]

3.5 THE HUMAN FACTOR

At this point the baker has developed a model that analyzes explicitly the technical and economic phases of the problem. What about the human phases? Is the optimum economic solution a practical one in terms of the people involved? Suppose, for example, that the baker and his helpers enjoy making iced cookies more than plain sugar cookies. This means that the over-all objective function should be the maximization of some combination of dollar contribution and enjoyment. Developing an explicit statement of this function is extremely difficult, if not impossible. We can, however, take this intangible factor into account in the final stages of our analysis, as shown in Table 3.5.

TABLE 3.5

Point	Production: Iced	Production: Sugar	Dollar Contribution	Enjoyment	Total Satisfaction
A	0 dozen	0 dozen	$ 0.00	Nil	Nil
B	80 "	0 "	16.00	Maximum	?
C	80 "	30 "	20.50	Great	?
D	60 "	60 "	21.00	Moderate	?
E	0 "	120 "	18.00	Nil	?

[12] Presumably, he should have asked and answered these questions in the negative *before* he began his analysis. Good practice dictates that one review the nature of all basic assumptions *after* the analysis as well.

We cannot fill in all of the Total Satisfaction column until the baker, using judgment, evaluates it for us. He might decide, for example, that it was "worth" 50¢ per day to him to be allowed to produce 80 dozen iced cookies and only 30 dozen sugar cookies (point *C*). On the other hand, he might also decide that the loss of an additional $4.50 required to avoid the production of any sugar cookies (point *B*) was not acceptable to him. In this case the optimal decision, considering all phases of the problem, would be the product mix indicated by point *C*.

3.6 SUMMARY

The graphical method is capable of handling linear programming problems of only limited complexity and is, therefore, a special rather than a general method. The most limiting factor is the number of variables involved. A two-dimensional graphical display of relationships is restricted to two independent variables.

The two basic assumptions common to all linear programming methods — linearity and certainty — are recognized explicitly both in framing the problem and in solving it.

Except in special cases, the optimal solution will always lie at one of the several points or vertices of the polygon of technical feasibility. The search for these points is made more effective by the visual display of the relationships among variables and constraints.

The precision of solutions developed by purely graphical solution methods is a function of the scale and accuracy of the graphical display. The accuracy of solutions may be improved through the use of algebraic methods. In such cases the graphical portion of the analysis becomes of secondary importance.

Most of the technical and economic phases of a problem may be expressed explicitly and treated directly in the analysis. Many qualitative and intangible human factors cannot be handled in this manner. The primary contribution of any quantitative method is in narrowing the judgment portion of decision-making, not in eliminating it. It is important, therefore, to recognize that the optimal solution from a linear programming model is not necessarily an optimal over-all solution to the problem. Managerial judgment rather than mathematics must be used in large part for the selection of the best alternative course of action and, of course, for the implementation of the decision.

3.7 REVIEW QUESTIONS

1. What are restrictions or constraints? What is their net effect on the number of alternatives open to the decision-maker?

2. Justify the use of maximization of total dollar contribution to fixed costs and profit as the objective function in the quantitative portion of the analysis for the bakery problem.

3. Show specifically where the two basic assumptions of linear programming — linearity and certainty — enter into the analysis.

4. Why, except in special cases, does the solution always lie at one of the points or vertices of the technical feasibility polygon?

5. Under what circumstances would there be a range of optimal solutions? How could the decision-maker go about selecting a final alternative from this optimal range?

6. Linear programming is sometimes described as effective search procedure. Explain the meaning of this statement.

7. Explain briefly the purpose and content of Table 3.5. Give specific reasons for including question marks in the final column.

3.8 EXERCISES

1. Determine the optimal product mix for the bakery problem discussed in the chapter on the basis of the following contributions:

a. $C_I = 25¢$ and $C_S = 15¢$

b. $C_I = 30¢$ and $C_S = 20¢$

2. The Zeus Company manufactures a deluxe and a standard model. All production is to stock rather than to customer order.

At the present time a seller's market exists for the company's products. Although the Zeus Company has made no attempt to charge prices other than those that they have charged for several years, they are concerned with the profitability of their product mix. The profit contribution of the deluxe model is $3.00 per unit and that of the standard model is $1.00 per unit.

The manufacture of the product is relatively simple. Both models require a machining operation, and the deluxe model requires an additional painting operation. The same machines are used for machining either model. Since all units are placed in inventory before being sold, warehouse capacity as well as equipment capacities must be considered in making product mix decisions.

The technical requirements and restrictions, on a monthly basis, are as follows:

	Resource Requirements		
	Machining (machine hours per piece)	Warehousing (square feet per piece)	Painting (man hours per piece)
Standard	2	4	0
Deluxe	3	3	1
Total Capacities Available	24,000	36,000	6,000

a. Determine the most profitable mix for next month.

b. Determine the best mix if the contributions of the two products were reversed, if $C_S = \$3$, $C_D = \$1$.

c. In general, what effects would changes in the contribution ratio have on the solution? Show specifically where changes in the solution occur.

d. Under what circumstances would there be a range of equally profitable product mixes for The Zeus Company? (Hint: This would be a very special case. A very careful answer to Question (c) will help you.)

e. What are the linear characteristics of the problem?

f. In what respects is the human element considered in this problem?

3. The Lotanoiz Corporation manufactures a "Hollywood" automobile muffler in one size only. However, they produce two models — the "Long-Life" and the "Economuf." The "Long-Life" is of heavier metal construction and also receives a special alloy dipping before being painted.

Since the corporation is young and operates on a comparatively small margin of profit, the owner-managers are very anxious to find the exact product mix that will yield maximum return. At present, both types of mufflers are selling quite well and neither model seems to have the better market potential.

Model	Total Direct Man Hours Required for Fabrication per Unit	Time Required per Pair for Dipping Operation (Hours)	Time Required per Pair for Painting (Hours)	Contribution per Unit
Economuf	1.0	—	0.1	\$0.80
Long-Life	1.5	0.2	0.1	\$0.90

Painting operations may be carried on 37.5 hours per week. Two units are painted at a time. The dipping operation can be carried on 8 hours per day (5 days per week). Two units may be dipped at a time. As both mufflers are the same size, the shipping department can process up to 800 units weekly regardless of the model mix. A total of 900 man-hours is available per week in the fabricating department.

(a) Given the information provided above, what weekly production schedule would you suggest?

(b) Which departments will be operating at capacity if your schedule is adopted? How much idle capacity will exist in those departments that are operating at less than full capacity?

(c) What could the management of the Lotanoiz Corporation do to "relax" the various technical restrictions in this problem, that is, to move the restrictions further away from the origin? To which ones should their initial efforts be directed? Why?

4. The Plummer Company produces two types of men's billfolds. The higher-priced Chieftain line uses more first grade materials and is virtually hand-made. The lower-priced Warrior line is largely machine-made and uses a higher percentage of standard grade materials. Each Chieftain unit contributes $5.00 and each Warrior unit contributes $3.00 toward overhead and profit.

The firm has been producing 600 of the Chieftain model and 300 of the Warrior model every week. The most recent sales forecast indicates that these figures represent maximum possible sales during the next week as well. The company's labor force of ten skilled long-service employees work 36-hour weeks.

The company's suppliers have just notified them that due to a temporary shortage of materials no shipments can be made for at least one week. This means that the materials now available, the sales forecast, and labor availability must be considered in developing next week's schedule.

The material requirements and labor hour availability are as follows:

	Chieftain	*Warrior*	*Available*
First grade materials	.4 sq ft per unit	.2 sq ft per unit	256 sq ft
Standard materials	.3 sq ft per unit	.5 sq ft per unit	276 sq ft
Labor	.5 hrs per unit	.2 hrs per unit	360 hrs/week

a. The sales manager has proposed that only Chieftain models be produced next week because of its higher contribution.

(1) Frame the problem in a graphical format.

(2) Evaluate the sales manager's proposal.

b. The production engineer suggests that any reduction of work hours should be held to an absolute minimum. He proposes that the schedule adopted should be that one which will maximize the number of employees' hours to be worked during the week.

(1) Evaluate this proposal.

4 ▸ THE SIMPLEX METHOD

4.1 GENERAL NATURE OF THE METHOD

ANY PROBLEM that fits the two basic assumptions of linear programming can be solved by the simplex method. It is, in fact, the general method, as differentiated from the graphical, transportation, and other special methods. This broad capability is gained, from the student's viewpoint at least, only at the expense of a considerable increase in mathematical complexity. The term "simplex" is somewhat misleading; it is actually the most difficult method to comprehend. The reader who fully understands the graphical method, however, should not find it too difficult.

The basic problem in linear programming is to find the particular set of variables that satisfies all constraints and maximizes — or minimizes — the value of the objective function. The orderly solution of problems using the simplex format requires the performance of a series of carefully defined steps. The purpose of the procedure is to produce the desired result with minimum computation effort.

The major advantage of the graphical method is that the visual display of relationships enables the analyst to see the points on the polygon of technical feasibility. Since the optimal solution ordinarily lies at one of these vertices, the search procedure may be limited to an analysis of these points. Theoretically, a three-dimensional display might be useful in problems involving three variables. Constraints in this case would become planes, as would the objective function, and the optimal solution would represent one of the many intersections generated by these planes.

Most linear programming problems that lend themselves to analysis by the simplex method involve many more than three variables. It would be most difficult to visualize a five-dimensional problem, let alone a twenty-dimensional problem. Nevertheless, it is useful in understanding the rationale of the simplex method to attempt certain analogies. One such analogy is to compare the computation procedure to that of developing a plan for climbing a mountain. The objective may be stated simply: to reach the summit (maximize the objective function). There would be, presumably, an infinite number of routes that might be taken by the climbers. If the mountain were high, it might be necessary to accomplish the total task in stages. Intuitive reasoning would indicate that as long as each of these camps is higher up the mountain than the previous one, the party will progress toward the summit. Thus, many alternative routes can be eliminated even though they are feasible.[1] Starting from the base (origin), an effective climbing procedure (computation procedure) would reach the summit (optimal solution) with a minimum number of camps (steps or iterations).

Mountains, of course, have only three rather than five or twenty dimensions. At the same time, the simplex procedure can and does "reach the summit" of linear programming problems having many variables.

---

[1] For example, a climbing plan that establishes camp 1 at 10,000 feet, camp 2 at 5,000 feet, camp 3 at 8,000 feet, and camp 4 at 2,000 feet, is feasible but ridiculous in terms of the objective.

4.2 COMPUTATION PROCEDURE

1. Frame the problem.
   a. Select the pertinent variables and constraints.
   b. Express the relationship between all variables and constraints in explicit form, that is, in equations.
   c. Determine the objective function or measure of effectiveness.
2. Develop an initial feasible solution.
   a. Technically, any basic feasible solution is acceptable.
   b. For practical purposes, the origin solution is usually selected.
3. Evaluate the alternative variables that might be brought into the solution. Several methods of evaluation may be used, including:
   a. Net effect per unit.
   b. Net total effect.
4. Select one of the variables and determine the number of units of each variable represented by the revised solution.
5. Make the necessary adjustments to express the new rates of substitution between those variables in the solution and all variables.
6. Repeat Steps 3, 4, and 5 until an analysis at Step 3 reveals that no additional changes of a favorable nature can be made.

4.3 PRODUCT-MIX EXAMPLE

The product-mix problem represents an elementary problem capable of analysis by the simplex as well as by the graphical method. Let us, therefore, rework the problem using the simplex format.

4.31 Step 1. The relationship between variables and constraints must be expressed in equations rather than by the visual presentation acceptable in the graphical method.

The total demand for the direct labor resource is determined by the number of each type of cookie in the solution at any point. Each dozen iced cookies introduced into the product mix will require the allocation of .15 direct labor hours. Similarly, each dozen sugar cookies produced requires .10 labor hours. Furthermore, only those combinations that require a total of 15 or less hours are feasible solutions, as shown below:

Labor hours (iced) + Labor hours (sugar) $\leqq$ Total labor available

This is an inequality; the two sides are not always equal to one another. It can be converted into an equation by adding unused, idle, or "slack" capacity (resources) to the left side, as follows:

Labor hours (iced) + Labor hours (sugar) + Labor hours (slack) = Total labor hours available

The two sides of this expression will always be equal. It is necessary, however, to make the expression more specific for it to be useful in the simplex analysis:

Labor hours (iced) = $.15\ Q_I$, where Q_I = dozens of iced cookies

Labor hours (sugar) = $.10\ Q_S$, where Q_S = dozens of sugar cookies

Thus:

$$.15\ Q_I + .10\ Q_S + \text{Labor hours (slack)} = 15 \qquad (4.1)$$

For computation purposes it is necessary to express the slack capacity in the same general form as the real variables. A useful convention is to assume that fictitious products are produced with those capacities not required by the real variables in the solution. For example, suppose that some imaginary cookie (type *L*) can be produced with the slack labor capacity. The symbol Q_L would represent the number of dozens produced. If each dozen *L* cookies is assumed to require 1.0 hours of labor capacity and no other resources, then 1.0 Q_L represents the demand on the labor resource to produce Q_L dozens.[2] The supply and demand equation for the labor resource may now be written as:

$$.15\ Q_I + .10\ Q_S + 1.0\ Q_L = 15 \tag{4.2}$$

This equation means that the sum of the labor requirements for iced, sugar, and *L* cookies is always equal to 15 hours. The requirement for *L* cookies is a mathematical fact but a fiction in reality, since it actually represents that portion of labor capacity not required for the real variables.

Let *O* cookies represent the slack variable for unused oven capacity and *M* cookies the corresponding slack variable for icing mix.[3] The complete set of relationships between all five variables — two real and three slack — and the labor constraint may now be expressed as follows:

$$.15\ Q_I + .10\ Q_S + 1.0\ Q_L + 0.0\ Q_O + 0.0\ Q_M = 15 \tag{4.3}$$

where:

Q_I = dozens of iced cookies
Q_S = dozens of sugar cookies
} real variables

Q_L = dozens of *L* cookies
Q_O = dozens of *O* cookies
Q_M = dozens of *M* cookies
} slack variables

[2] The assumption of 1.0 labor hour is based on computation convenience. Technically, any positive number would be an acceptable assumption. Note also that slack variables are assumed to require only the resource for which they represent idle capacity. Thus, the "recipe" for *L* cookies calls for 1.0 hour of labor capacity and zero icing mix and oven capacity.

[3] Using the procedure suggested in footnote 2, the "recipe" for *O* cookies calls for 1.0 unit of oven capacity per dozen. Making *M* cookies requires 1.0 pound of icing mix per dozen.

Eq. (4.3) differs from Eq. (4.2) only in that the relationship between the two slack variables representing oven and icing mix resources have been added to the expression. Their coefficients are zero since their production requires no labor capacity. The addition of these two terms does not add to the "practical" meaning of the equation but it does satisfy one of the basic requirements of the simplex method, that all relationships between variables and restrictions must be stated explicitly and completely.

Similar expressions representing the relationship between all five variables and the oven and icing mix capacities may now be derived as follows:

Oven capacity (iced) + Oven capacity (sugar) $\leq$ Total oven capacity

This inequality can be converted into an equation by adding a third term representing that portion of total capacity not required by the two real products. The total oven capacity is given as 120 dozen per day. The equation thus becomes:

Oven capacity (iced) + Oven capacity (sugar) + Oven capacity (slack) = 120

Each dozen iced and sugar cookies will require 1.0 unit of the total oven capacity. The *O* cookies, the variable representing slack oven capacity, are assumed, for computation convenience, to require 1.0 unit of oven capacity and no other resources:

$$1.0\, Q_I + 1.0\, Q_S + 1.0\, Q_O = 120$$

Finally, the addition of the two additional slack variables (*L* and *M* cookies) to the equation will represent the complete set of relationships between all variables and the oven capacity constraint:

$$1.0\, Q_I + 1.0\, Q_S + 0.0\, Q_L + 1.0\, Q_O + 0.0\, Q_M = 120 \qquad (4.4)$$

Note that the coefficients of Q_L and Q_M are zero in

this equation, since neither of these variables requires any oven capacity.

Only one real and one slack variable make a demand on the icing mix resource — iced cookies and *M* cookies (the slack variable for icing mix). The recipe for iced cookies requires .4 pounds per dozen, and *M* cookies, by definition require 1.0 pound per dozen. The amount of icing mix on hand is equal to 32 pounds. Thus, the complete set of relationships would be:

$$.4\,Q_I + 0.0\,Q_S + 0.0\,Q_L + 0.0\,Q_O + 1.0\,Q_M = 32 \quad (4.5)$$

The coefficients of Q_S, Q_L, and Q_O are zero, since their production would not require any of the icing mix resource.

It is more convenient for computation purposes to express the relationships between variables and constraints in the form of a table than to retain the expressions in their more familiar equation form. The general format for such a presentation is given in Table 4.1.

TABLE 4.1

Variables	Q_I	Q_S	Q_L	Q_O	Q_M	Capacity
Labor	.15	.10	1	0	0	15
Oven	1.0	1.0	0	1	0	120
Icing Mix	.4	.0	0	0	1	32

The columns in the table represent the recipes for the various products (variables) in the problem. For example, reading down the column headed by the symbol Q_I reproduces the requirements for iced cookies, .15 labor hours, 1.0 unit of oven capacity, and .4 pounds of icing mix per dozen. Similarly, each dozen sugar cookies requires .10 labor hours, 1.0 unit of oven capacity, and zero icing mix. The requirements for all slack variables are unique in that, by definition, they require 1.0 unit of the capacity they represent and nothing more. Just as sugar cookies require no icing mix, L cookies (the variable that represents slack labor capacity) require no oven capacity or icing mix. In like manner, O cookies require only oven capacity and M cookies require icing mix but no labor or oven capacity.

Equations (4.3), (4.4), and (4.5) may be reproduced from Table 4.1 by multiplying each of the series of coefficients in each row by the appropriate Q, which appears at the head of each column. For example, the first row produces

$$(.15)\, Q_I + (.10)\, Q_S + (1)\, Q_L + (0)\, Q_O + (0)\, Q_M = 15.$$

Similar interpretation of the second row shows that this row reproduces Eq. (4.4) and that the third row represents Eq. (4.5).

The objective function, as such, does not appear in these tables. The general form of this equation was formulated in the graphical example (Sec. 3.3) as:

$$Q_I \times C_I + Q_S \times C_S = TC$$

where:

C_I = contribution per dozen iced cookies

C_S = contribution per dozen sugar cookies

TC = total contribution to fixed costs and profit

The requirements of the simplex method have, however, made it necessary to introduce three additional variables into the problem. Thus, a complete statement of the objective function must include the "contribution" of the slack as well as of the real variables, as follows:

$$Q_I \times C_I + Q_S \times C_S + Q_L \times C_L + Q_O \times C_O + Q_M \times C_M = TC$$

What values should be assigned to C_L, C_O, and C_M, that is what addition to the total dollar contribution results from the addition of one dozen L, O, or M cookies to the product mix? Since these are fictitious products introduced to represent slack capacity, their economic contribution should represent the value of slack capacity. By implication the contribution of slack resources in the graphical method was zero; unused capacity resulted in no additional income or costs. In accordance with the need for explicit relationships in the simplex method, assume that C_L, C_O, and C_M are zero. Thus:

$$Q_I \times 20¢ + Q_S \times 15¢ + Q_L \times 0¢ + Q_O \times 0¢ + Q_M \times 0¢ = TC \tag{4.6}$$

This information concerning the relative economic values of the variables can now be added to the computation table. By convention these values are placed above the corresponding Q term at the head of each column, as in Table 4.2.

TABLE 4.2

Contribution Variables	20¢ Q_I	15¢ Q_S	0¢ Q_L	0¢ Q_O	0¢ Q_M	Capacity
Labor	.15	.10	1	0	0	15
Oven	1.0	1.0	0	1	0	120
Icing Mix	.4	0.0	0	0	1	32

The information presented in Table 4.2 can be summarized as follows:

a. There are five variables in the problem. Only two of these (iced and sugar cookies) are real variables. The three slack variables (*L, O,* and *M* cookies) are fictitious products introduced into the problem because of the necessity for explicit relationships. In reality, these slack variables represent unused or idle capacity in the labor, oven, and icing mix resources.
b. The numbers in the columns below each variable indicate the resources required to produce one unit of each variable.
c. The numbers in the rows show the relationship between each variable in the problem and each resource of limited capacity (restrictions or constraints).

d. The economic values above each variable indicate the contribution to the objective function or measure of effectiveness that results from the introduction of one unit of each variable into the solution. In the bakery problem these values represent the contribution to profit and fixed costs that results from the production of one dozen of each type of cookie. Only real products have positive contributions. Slack variables normally have zero values since they represent fictitious products that cost nothing to produce and have no market value.

4.32 Step 2 (Explanation). The computation procedure for the simplex method is actually a method of hunting for better and better solutions until the optimal solution is discovered. Theoretically, the solution of a simplex problem may be started at any one of the several basic solutions,[4] but for practical reasons the origin solution should be chosen as the initial solution since it is the easiest to visualize and to formulate.

The origin solution is represented by point *A* in Figure 3.6 (page 31). It is a technically feasible solution which, in the graphical analysis, was interpreted to mean that no cookie production takes place. Because this solution made no economic sense, the succeeding stages of the graphical analysis proceeded to move or change the product mix to those represented by other points on the feasibility polygon.

The meaning of an origin solution in the simplex method is somewhat different than in the graphical method. No real variables are produced. This means that all resources are idle insofar as iced and sugar cookies are concerned. Remember, however, that slack variables were defined as that portion of each resource not required for the production of real products. Therefore, the origin solution in the simplex method represents a solution that calls for the production of slack variables only. This makes no more economic sense than the origin solution in the graphical

---

[4] A basic solution is defined as a solution at one of the points or vertices of the polygon of technical feasibility. Points *A, B, C, D,* and *E* in Figure 3-6 represent the basic solutions for this problem.

method, but it does provide a useful starting point from which better solutions may be developed.

In the bakery example, the origin solution indicates that no iced or sugar cookies are to be produced and that all resources are to be allocated to the production of slack products (*L, O,* and *M* cookies). What quantities of each type are in the product mix at this point? Reference to Table 4.2 shows that 15 hours of direct labor are available. The only slack product that requires this resource is *L* cookies, so that the entire 15 hours may be devoted to their production. The first coefficient under Q_L in the table indicates that one hour of direct labor is required per dozen *L* cookies. The number of *L* cookies in the origin solution is, therefore, 15 dozen ($15 \div 1 = 15$). Similar reasoning applied to the other slack variables leads to the conclusion that the 120-dozen oven capacity should be used to produce 120 dozen *O* cookies and that the 32 pounds of icing mix should be allocated to the production of 32 dozen *M* cookies. In summary, the product mix indicated by the origin solution in the simplex method would be:

$$Q_I = 0, Q_S = 0, Q_L = 15, Q_O = 120, Q_M = 32$$

For computation purposes the origin solution must be shown in tabular form, as in Table 4.3.

TABLE 4.3

Contribution Variables	20¢ Q_I	15¢ Q_S	0¢ Q_L	0¢ Q_O	0¢ Q_M	Production
0¢ Q_L	.15	.10	1	0	0	15 Dozen *L* cookies
0¢ Q_O	1.0	1.0	0	1	0	120 Dozen *O* cookies
0¢ Q_M	.4	0.0	0	0	1	32 Dozen *M* cookies

Note that this table differs from Table 4.2 in two respects. First, the variables presently in the solution are shown on the left side of the table together with their economic values. The fact that these are all slack variables identifies the solution as that of the origin. Secondly, the title of the final column in the table has been changed from "Capacity" to "Production." Of course, the production of 15 dozen *L* cookies, 120 dozen *O* cookies, and 32 dozen *M* cookies actually represents idle capacity in the labor, oven, and icing-mix resources. The adoption of this fiction was necessary to meet the needs of the simplex computation framework. It is, however, an assumption that tries the patience of the reader who finds it difficult to describe "idle capacity" by any other term.

4.33 Steps 3 and 4 (Explanation and Analysis). Of the five variables in the baking problem, only two — iced cookies and sugar cookies — were not included in the product mix represented by the origin solution. Would the introduction of either of these products into the solution improve the economic performance of the system? Answering this question is the objective of Step 3 in the simplex computation procedure.

The production of each dozen iced cookies would add a 20¢ contribution to fixed costs and overhead. The data for this product (see column of coefficients under Q_{I} in Table 4.2) shows that the production of each dozen iced cookies requires the allocation of .15 labor hours, 1 unit of oven capacity, and .4 pounds of icing mix. In the special language of the simplex method (see Table 4.3), the introduction of one dozen iced cookies into the solution would require that some portion of the variables in the existing solution be "given up." The specific products and amounts that would have to be withdrawn for each dozen iced cookies introduced would be .15 dozen *L* cookies, 1 dozen *O* cookies, and .4 dozen *M* cookies. Since the economic contribution of these slack products by definition is zero, this exchange of real products for slack variables would appear to be a worthwhile one. Similarly, the substitution of sugar cookies for slack variables would also be a favorable change. It is necessary, therefore, to make a detailed analysis of the consequences of these two alternative changes in the product mix to determine which is most favorable.

Alternative No. 1 — Add iced cookies to product mix.

(1) Add: 1 dozen iced cookies having an economic value of 20¢ per dozen. Gross gain per unit = 20¢.

(2) Less: value of products given up to permit production of each dozen iced cookies.

$$
\begin{aligned}
.15 \text{ dozen } L \text{ cookies @ } 0¢ \text{ per dozen} &= .15 \times 0¢ = 0¢ \\
1.0 \text{ dozen } O \text{ cookies @ } 0¢ \text{ per dozen} &= 0¢ \\
.4 \text{ dozen } M \text{ cookies @ } 0¢ \text{ per dozen} &= \underline{0¢} \\
\text{Contribution loss per dozen} &= 0¢
\end{aligned}
$$

(3) The net change in contribution for each dozen iced cookies introduced is the difference between the value of the variable introduced and the variables given up to make this possible (20¢ − 0¢ = 20¢ per gain per dozen).

Alternative No. 2 — Add sugar cookies to product mix.

(1) Gross gain = 15¢ per dozen.

(2) Value of products displaced in product mix by each dozen sugar cookies introduced.

$$
\begin{aligned}
1.0 \text{ dozen } O \text{ cookies @ } 0¢ &= 0¢ \\
.10 \text{ dozen } L \text{ cookies @ } 0¢ &= 0¢
\end{aligned}
$$

Loss of contribution = 0¢

(3) Net gain per dozen sugar cookies introduced = 15¢ − 0¢ = 15¢

One criterion that may be used to select the alternative variable to be introduced at any stage of a simplex problem is that of net effect per unit on the measure of effectiveness or objective function. At this stage of the bakery example, this criterion would indicate that iced rather than sugar cookies should be brought into the product mix since they have a higher net contribution to profit and overhead per dozen.[5]

[5] This same conclusion was reached in the early stages of the graphical method analysis on the basis of their contribution per dozen. The simplex may seem like "the hard way" in this and other respects. Remember, however, that the simplex is also the only way of solving problems of this type that involve more than two variables.

A second criterion that may be used in selecting from among the alternative variables that might be introduced is that of net total effect on the objective function. This is defined as the product of the net effect per unit and the number of units that could be introduced at that stage of the solution.[6] Since the net contributions per dozen have already been determined, it is now necessary to determine the number of dozens of iced and sugar cookies that might be introduced into the origin solution.

The number of units that might be introduced is determined, as in the graphical example, by the restrictions.[7]

A. If iced cookies are introduced (move from A toward B in Figure 3.3):
   1. *L* cookies (labor capacity) must be given up.
      a. Each dozen iced cookies displaces .15 dozen *L* cookies.
      b. The limit or restriction for *L* cookies is 15 dozen.
      c. The maximum number of iced cookies that may be introduced in terms of this restriction is, therefore, 100 dozen (point *F* in Figure 3.3).
   2. *O* cookies (idle oven capacity) must also be given up.
      a. Each dozen iced cookies displaces 1.0 dozen *O* cookies.
      b. The restriction on *O* cookies is 120 dozen.
      c. The maximum number of iced cookies that may be introduced in terms of this restriction is 120 (point *G* in Figure 3.3).
   3. In addition, *M* cookies (idle icing mix) must also be given up.
      a. The rate of substitution or exchange between iced cookies and *M* cookies is 1.0 to .4, each one dozen

[6] A significant advantage of the total effect criterion, especially when hand computation methods are being used, is that it should produce an optimum solution in the fewest total number of tables. In this particular problem it will require only three tables rather than the four needed by the per unit criterion.

[7] The computations which follow are based on the data in Table 4.3 (page 50). The graphical interpretations are drawn from Fig. 3.3 (page 24).

iced cookies displaces .4 dozen *M* cookies.

b. The restriction on *M* cookies is 32 dozen.

c. Limit on iced cookies corresponding to this restriction is 80 (point *B* in Figure 3.3).

4. The most limiting restriction for iced cookies is *M* cookies. Therefore, the number of iced cookies that could be introduced at this stage is limited to 80 dozen. (Move to point B in Figure 3.3 (page 24). Solutions *F* and *G* are not technically feasible.)

5. If 80 dozen iced cookies are brought into the solution, what quantity of the slack products that were represented in the origin solution will be displaced? The coefficients of Table 4.3 show that .15 dozen *L* cookies (actually .15 hours of labor capacity) must be given up for each dozen iced cookies introduced. Thus, $(80 \times .15 = 12)$ dozen are displaced. Since the total dozens of *L* cookies in the origin solution was 15, 3 dozen remain.[8]

   Q_L (second stage) $= 15 - 80 \times .15 = 3$ dozen *L* cookies

   Similar reasoning indicates that the values for Q_O and Q_M at the second stage would be:

   Q_O (second stage) $= 120 - 80 \times 1.0 = 40$ (point *G* – point *B*)

   Q_M (second stage) $= 32 - 80 \times .4 = 0$ (out of solution at point *B*; no idle icing mix would be available for the production of *M* cookies).

   Therefore, if 80 dozen iced cookies were to be introduced, the variables in the second solution and their quantities would be $Q_I = 80$, $Q_L = 3$, and $Q_O = 40$.

6. The total net change in the objective function Eq. (4.6) corresponding to this change in variables would be as follows:

   a. The new value of the objective function (at point *B*), $TC = 80 \times 20¢ + 0 \times 15¢ + 3 \times 0¢ + 40 \times 0¢ + 0 \times 0¢ = \$16.00$

---

[8] Note that 3 hours of labor capacity would be sufficient to produce 20 dozen iced cookies $(3 \div .15)$. This is the difference between points *F* and *B* in Figure 3.3.

b. Less the previous value of the objective function (origin), $TC = 0 \times 20¢ + 0 \times 15¢ + 15 \times 0¢ + 120 \times 0¢ + 32 \times 0¢ = \$0.00$
c. Net change = \$16.00 − 0.00 = \$16.00

B. If sugar rather than iced cookies were to be introduced (move from *A* toward point *E* in Figure 3.3):

1. *L* cookies must be allocated to production of sugar cookies.
   a. Limit on sugar cookies would be 150 dozen (15÷.10).
2. *O* cookies must also be given up.
   a. Limit is 120 (120 ÷ 1.0).
3. *M* cookies must also be given up.
   a. Limit = infinity (32 ÷ 0), since sugar cookies require no icing mix.
4. Most limiting restriction is *O* cookies.
5. If $Q_S = 120$, then slack production would be:
   $Q_O = 120 - 120 \times 1.0 = 0$ (Now out of solution)
   $Q_L = 15 - .10 \times 120 = 3$
   $Q_M = 32 - 120 \times 0.0 = 32$
6. Net change in objective function:
   a. New value = \$18.00 (point *E*)
   b. Previous value = \$0.00 (point *A*)
   c. Net change = \$18.00

C. Conclusion: Sugar cookies should be introduced since the net total contribution of this variable at this stage of the analysis is greater (\$18.00) than that of iced cookies (\$16.00).

D. The variables in the second stage solution and the quantities of each would be (from Step B-5 above):

$$Q_S = 120, Q_L = 3, Q_M = 32.$$

Both Q_I and Q_O are, of course, still in the problem but are not in the solution, since they are zero at this stage of the problem.

The initial purpose of Step 3 in the simplex procedure is to determine if the introduction of any of the problem variables not in the existing solution (origin solution, in this case) would have a favorable effect on the objective function. The method of analysis used to evaluate this condition is to determine the net effect per dozen of iced and sugar cookies. Both have favorable effects in this case because the only products displaced are slack variables.

The method suggested here for selecting the variable to be introduced is the use of a net total effect criterion. This requires that the maximum number of units that could be introduced be determined for both iced and sugar cookies.

The net change in contribution was found to be 80 dozen × 20¢ per dozen or $16.00 for iced cookies, and 120 dozen × 15¢ per dozen or $18.00 for sugar cookies.

It was concluded from the analysis of Step 3 that 120 dozen sugar cookies should be added to the product mix represented by the existing (origin) solution. As a consequence, it was then necessary to determine the number of dozens of the slack products (actually, amounts of the various resources) that were displaced by the introduction of the sugar cookies and the amounts remaining in the solution.

The graphical analogy of these computations is "moving" from point *A* to point *E*. At point *E*, 120 sugar cookies and zero iced cookies are being produced, the oven capacity is fully utilized, all of the icing mix capacity remains idle, and only 12 of the 15 labor hours are required. The simplex states that:

$$Q_S = 120$$
$$Q_I = 0$$
$$Q_O = 0$$
$$Q_M = 32$$
$$Q_L = 3$$

4.34 Step 5. It is necessary to develop a table to represent the "solution" at each stage of the search procedure. Some of the necessary information to construct a second table for the bakery example was developed in the later stages of Steps 3 and 4. This information is shown in Table 4.4.

TABLE 4.4

Contribution Variables	20¢ Q_I	15¢ Q_S	0¢ Q_L	0¢ Q_O	0¢ Q_M	Production
0¢ Q_L						3 Dozen *L* cookies
15¢ Q_S						120 Dozen Sugar cookies
0¢ Q_M						32 Dozen *M* cookies

Note that the middle row heading has changed, since sugar cookies have displaced *O* cookies in the origin solution. The production figures have also changed, due to the change in product mix adopted in Step 4.

The most trying computation task associated with the simplex method is the determination of the new coefficients for Table 4.4. Most of the coefficients in Table 4.3 are no longer applicable since they represented the rates of substitution between all possible variables and the variables in the solution at that time. The new set of coefficients may be determined from the former set. From Table 4.3:

$$S = (.10\,L) + (1.0\,O) + (0.0\,M)$$

This expression represents the original recipe for sugar cookies. It was very useful in the graphical method in that it indicated what resources and amounts must be allocated to the production of sugar cookies as the solution (product mix) was moved from point *A* to point *E*. It was also a useful expression in Steps 3 and 4 of the simpler method inasmuch as it showed exactly what quantities of the variables in the solution (all slacks at the origin) had to be given up to produce each dozen sugar cookies.

Having arrived at a second-stage solution in the simplex method, the mathematical equivalent of point E, Table 4.4 does an adequate job of describing the product mix ($Q_L = 3$, $Q_S = 120$, and $Q_M = 32$) in its present form. What is needed now is a new set of coefficients, which describe the exchange rates or rates of substitution between the new set of variables in the solution (L, S, and M) and all variables in the problem (I, S, L, O, and M).

Solving the original sugar cookie recipe for O produces the following expression:

$$O = S - (.10\,L) - (0.0\,M) \tag{4.7}$$

By substituting the right-hand side of Eq. (4.7) for O wherever the latter is found in the "recipes" applicable to the origin solution, a new set of coefficients will be found that are relevant to the second-stage solution.
For example, from Table 4.3:

$$\begin{aligned} I &= .15\,L + 1.0\,(O) + .4\,M \text{ (original coefficients)} \\ &= .15\,L + 1.0\,(S - .10\,L - 0.0\,M) + .4\,M \\ &= .05\,L + 1.0\,S + .4\,M \end{aligned} \tag{4.8}$$

$$\begin{aligned} L &= 1.0\;\; L + 0\,(O) + 0\,(M) \\ &= 1.0\;\; L + 0\,(S - .10\,L - 0.0\,M) + 0\,(M) \\ &= 1.0\;\; L + 0\,(S) + 0\,(M) \end{aligned} \tag{4.9}$$

$$\begin{aligned} S &= .10\,L + 1.0\,O + 0.0\,M \\ &= .10\,L + 1.0\,(S - .10\,L - 0.0\,M) + 0.0\,M \\ &= 0.0\;\; L + 1.0\,S + 0.0\,M \end{aligned} \tag{4.10}$$

$$\begin{aligned} M &= 0.0\;\; (L) + 0.0\,(O) + 1.0\,(M) \\ &= 0.0\;\; L + 0.0\,(S - .10\,L - 0.0\,M) + 1.0\,M \\ &= 0.0\;\; L + 0.0\,S + 1.0\,M \end{aligned} \tag{4.11}$$

The coefficients of Eqs. (4.7) through (4.11) may now be transferred to the appropriate columns of the table describing the solution at the second stage (Table 4.5).

TABLE 4.5

Contribution Variables	20¢ Q_I	15¢ Q_S	0¢ Q_L	0¢ Q_O	0¢ Q_M	Production
0¢ Q_L	.05	0	1	−.10	0	3 Dozen L cookies
15¢ Q_S	1	1	0	1	0	120 Dozen sugar cookies
0¢ Q_M	.4	0	0	0	1	32 Dozen M cookies

The solution described is that defined by point E in Figures 3.3 and 3.6. The only "real" production is 120 dozen sugar cookies. In the graphical method it was acceptable to indicate that the product mix represented by this point did not require all of the labor or icing mix capacities. The amount of this slack capacity in the labor resource was defined as an amount equal to the production requirement for 30 dozen sugar cookies (point H − point E). In the simplex method, this slack is defined as the capacity required to produce 3 dozen L cookies. The latter may be converted back to the former through their ratio of labor requirements as follows:

One dozen L cookies require 1.0 labor hours
One dozen sugar cookies require .10 labor hours
The slack labor capacity at point E = 3 dozen L cookies or 30 dozen sugar cookies ($3 \div .10 = 30$).

The point to be stressed once again is that the use of slack variables does not change the essential structure of the problem.

The meaning of the coefficients in Table 4.5 may be interpreted as follows:

A. The introduction of each dozen *O* cookies into the solution indicated by Table 4.5 would require:
   1. Giving up one dozen sugar cookies because of limited oven capacity.
   2. This reduction in the number of sugar cookies will release labor capacity equal to .10 dozen *L* cookies. Thus, the negative coefficient of −.10 means that .10 dozen *L* cookies would be added to the product mix.
   3. There is no change in the output of *M* cookies (Q_M) since the coefficient is zero.[9]

B. The introduction of each dozen iced cookies requires giving up:
   1. One dozen sugar cookies.
   2. An additional .05 dozen *L* cookies.
   3. Four-tenths (.4) dozen *M* cookies.

C. Introduction of *L* or *M* cookies would have no effect on the solution. Present units in the solution would simply be exchanged on a one-for-one basis for new units. Similar reasoning may be applied to the introduction of sugar cookies.

4.35 Step 3, Second Stage. The evaluation process for Table 4.5 (using total effect criterion) may be facilitated by the use of a tabular presentation, as shown in Table 4.6. This table represents a tabular summary of the computations required in Steps 3 and 4. The general method for making these computations is the same as that given under these two steps for the first-stage solution. For that reason, they will only be summarized here:

A. Enter the gross gain for each variable.

B. Determine the loss of contribution due to the fact that a portion of the variables now in the solution must

[9] Note the similarity of reasoning (but differences in answers) between the substitution of *O* cookies for sugar cookies here and the substitution of sugar cookies for *O* cookies in connection with Table 4-3. Reintroduction of *O* cookies would, in effect, return the solution to that at the origin.

TABLE 4.6

Computation		Q_I	Q_S	Q_L	Q_O	Q_M
A. Gross gain per dozen		20¢	15¢	0¢	0¢	0¢
B. Loss per dozen	L	.05 × 0¢ = 0¢	0 × 0¢ = 0¢	1 × 0¢ = 0¢	−.10 × 0¢ = 0¢	0 × 0¢ = 0¢
	S	1 × 15¢ = 15¢	1 × 15¢ = 15¢	0 × 15¢ = 0¢	1 × 15¢ = 15¢	0 × 15¢ = 0¢
	M	.4 × 0¢ = 0¢	0 × 0¢ = 0¢	0 × 0¢ = 0¢	0 × 0¢ = 0¢	1 × 0¢ = 0¢
	Total	15¢	15¢	0¢	15¢	0¢
C. Net Change per dozen		20¢ − 15¢ = +5¢	15¢ − 15¢ = 0¢	0¢ − 0¢ = 0¢	0¢ − 15¢ = −15¢	0¢ − 0¢ = 0¢
D. Number of dozens	L	3 ÷ .05 = 60				
	S	120 ÷ 1 = 120				
	M	32 ÷ .4 = 80				
E. Total Change in Objective Function		60 × 5¢ = $3.00				

be given up in order to introduce other products. (Multiply coefficients for each variable by contribution of product given up.)

C. Find net change per unit by subtracting total of Computation B from Computation A for each variable. (Note that only iced cookies have a positive contribution at this stage of the analysis. Reintroducing *O* cookies would decrease the value of the objective function by 15¢ per dozen and return the solution to the origin.)

D. For all products having a favorable net effect per dozen (iced cookies only in this case), determine the most limiting restriction. (This is labor capacity in the case of iced cookies.)

E. Determine the total effect on the objective function for all variables that were carried through Step D.

It is not essential that a table such as 4.6 be constructed for each iteration. Once the reader understands the reasons for and the logic behind the computations involved, several shortcuts should be evident. For example, Computations C and D can be performed mentally from the data in Table 4.5.[10]

4.36 Step 4. The conclusion implied by Table 4.6 is that 60 dozen iced cookies should be brought into the solution. As a consequence, the number of sugar cookies will be reduced to 60 dozen ($120 - 1 \times 60 = 60$), the number of *M* cookies to 8 dozen ($32 - .4 \times 60 = 8$), and *L* cookies will be reduced to zero ($3 - 60 \times .05 = 0$). The corresponding value of the objective function (Eq. [4.6]) is now:

$$60 \times 20¢ + 60 \times 15¢ + 0 \times 0¢ + 0 \times 0¢ + 8 \times 0¢ = \$21.00$$

---

[10] Other evaluation procedures and notational methods will, no doubt, suggest themselves as the reader's experience with the simplex method increases. The important thing is to keep things straight rather than to follow the methods suggested here.

4.37 Step 5. Iced, sugar, and M cookies (idle icing mix) are now in the solution.[11] This means that another new set of relationships (coefficients) must be determined for the table that describes this solution. Since iced cookies replaced L cookies in the product mix, from Table 4.5:

$$I = (.05)L + (1)S + (.4)M$$

$$L = \frac{I - S - .4M}{.05} = 20I - 20S - 8M$$

$$\begin{aligned} O &= -.10(L) + 1.0(S) + 0.0(M) \\ &= -.10(20I - 20S - 8M) + 1.0(S) + 0(M) \\ &= -2(I) + 2(S) + .8(M) + 1(S) + 0(M) \\ &= -2(I) + 3(S) + .8(M) \end{aligned}$$

$$\begin{aligned} I &= .05(20I - 20S - 8M) + 1(S) + .4(M) \\ &= 1(I) - 1(S) - .4(M) + 1(S) + .4(M) \\ &= 1(I) + 0(S) + 0(M) \end{aligned}$$

The new rates of substitution, together with the other information developed in Step 4, may now be used to construct the table representing the third stage.

TABLE 4.7

Contribution Variables		20¢ Q_I	15¢ Q_S	0¢ Q_L	0¢ Q_O	0¢ Q_M	Production
20¢	Q_I	1	0	20	−2	0	60 Dozen iced cookies
15¢	Q_S	0	1	−20	3	0	60 Dozen sugar cookies
0¢	Q_M	0	0	−8	.8	1	8 Dozen M cookies

[11] This product mix is that represented by point D in Figure 3.3.

4.38 Step 3. Although the reader "knows" that the third-stage solution is optimal, the final step in the simplex method requires "proof" of this optimality; i.e., no variable has a favorable net effect per unit on the measure of effectiveness. The evaluation procedure, shown in Table 4.8, is based on the information given in Table 4.7.

Since no variable has a favorable effect on the objective function (note net change per dozen), it is not necessary to carry the computations further. The optimal product mix is, therefore, 60 dozen each of sugar and iced cookies. Technically, 8 dozen *M* cookies are also in the optimal mix but, since they represent a fictitious product, they are not a "real" portion of the answer. Actually, this means that 8 pounds of icing mix will remain on hand at the end of the day.

4.4 SUMMARY

The simplex is the general method of linear programming. Any allocation problem that involves linearity and certainty can be solved through the use of this method.

Any linear programming method may be likened to an effective search procedure. The purpose of the search is to find that set of values for all variables that is technically feasible and that optimizes an appropriate objective function. The term "effective" is used in the sense that an optimal solution is obtained with the least possible computation effort.

The simplex computation procedure is more complex than those of special methods such as the graphical and transportation methods because the absence of simplifying factors and assumptions makes it necessary to rely entirely on mathematical expressions.

The mathematics involved in the simplex method requires the use of equations rather than inequalities. To meet this requirement it is necessary to express unused or idle resources in the form of slack variables. In the bakery example, these

TABLE 4.8

Computation		Q_I	Q_S	Q_L	Q_O	Q_M
A. Gross gain per dozen		20¢	15¢	0¢	0¢	0¢
B. Loss per dozen	*I*	1 × 20¢ = 20¢	0 × 20¢ = 0¢	20 × 20¢ = $4.00	−2 × 20¢ = −40¢	0 × 20¢ = 0¢
	S	0 × 15¢ = 0¢	1 × 15¢ = 15¢	−20 × 15¢ = −$3.00	−3 × 15¢ = 45¢	0 × 15¢ = 0¢
	M	0 × 0¢ = 0¢	0 × 0¢ = 0¢	−8 × 0¢ = −0¢	.8 × 0¢ = 0¢	1 × 0¢ = 0¢
	Total	20¢	15¢	$1.00	5¢	0¢
C. Net change per dozen		20¢ − 20¢ = 0¢	15¢ − 15¢ = 0¢	0¢ − $1.00 = −$1.00	0¢ − 5¢ = −5¢	0¢ − 0¢ = 0¢

slack variables represented fictitious products that were, by definition, produced with all resources not required by real products in the problem.

It is customary to start a simplex analysis at the origin solution since this is the simplest of the many possible solutions to formulate. Subsequent steps in the procedure involve bringing into the solution those variables that are shown to have a favorable effect on the measure of effectiveness. When all such favorable alternatives have been exhausted, the optimal solution has been reached and the analysis completed.

As with any quantitative method of analysis, the optimal solution to a simplex analysis is optimal only in the sense that all pertinent factors in the problem have been treated explicitly in the analysis. Qualitative factors may require modification of this solution before a final decision can be made.

Most business problems that justify analysis within a simplex framework involve many variables and constraints. The use of a computer is, therefore, frequently required for economical computation. The most important steps in the problem-solving process from a managerial viewpoint are, therefore, those of framing the problem and evaluating the results of the analysis.

4.5 REVIEW QUESTIONS

1. Why is the simplex method the general method of linear programming?

2. Explain why all relationships between variables and restrictions must be stated in equation form in this method.

3. What are slack variables? Why are they necessary in the simplex method? What effect do they have on the "answers" to problems analyzed by this method?

4. What is meant by a basic solution? The "origin" solution? Why is the latter normally used as the initial solution?

5. What do the coefficients within a simplex table represent? Why is it necessary to compute a new set for each table in the analysis?

6. What criteria may be used in determining which variable to bring into the solution at each stage of the computation procedure? What specific advantage does the total effect criterion have?

7. How does one know when an optimal solution has been reached?

4.6 EXERCISES

1. Rework the bakery problem. Include cookie mix in your analysis and use contributions of 25¢ for iced and 15¢ for sugar cookies.
    a. Write the basic equations.
    b. Develop the origin solution.
    c. Determine which real product to introduce.
    d. Develop the second stage solution table.
    e. Carry your anaylsis to the optimum solution.
    f. Explain the meaning of your final solution.
2. Use the simplex method to frame and solve the Zeus Company problem in Section 3.8. Follow Steps (a) to (f) in Problem 1 above.
3. Solve the Lotanoiz Corporation problem in Section 3.8, using the simplex format.
4. Determine the optimal product mix for the Plummer Company (Section 3.8) by use of the simplex method.
5. The bakery manager is considering the introduction of a larger size sugar cookie ("Sugar Kings") into his product line. Several experimental batches have been produced and sold. Data collected during these runs indicate that: (a) 1.2 pounds of cookie mix and .12 hours of labor are required per dozen, and (b) direct costs should be 65¢ per dozen. Limited market experience suggests that 95¢ per dozen would be an appropriate initial price.

a. Given these new facts and assuming no change in the other factors in the bakery problem:
   (1) Write the set of linear equations which describes this three-product case.
   (2) Develop an origin solution.
   (3) Carry the problem to an optimum solution.
   (4) Frame the problem using a three-dimensional display. Explain your analysis by means of this diagram.

b. Suppose that the baker decides: (a) to limit his initial production of "Sugar Kings" to 20 dozen per day, and (b) to use the remaining resources for iced and regular sugar cookies.
   (1) Determine the optimal product mix and expected contribution per day.

5 ▸ THE TRANSPORTATION METHOD

5.1 GENERAL NATURE OF THE METHOD

COMPLEX ALLOCATION problems having certain characteristics may be solved by a special, highly simplified version of the simplex referred to as the transportation, distribution, or stepping-stone method of linear programming. It is especially appropriate for source-to-destination situations such as the transportation of goods from plants to distribution facilities. The same solution framework, however, may be applied to a wide variety of problems. Thus, the characteristics of the problem itself rather than its institutional or functional setting determine whether or not this method is applicable.

The key characteristic of such problems is homogeneity. All rates of substitution between variables must be one to one. Such a condition was illustrated in the bakery example by the relationship between the real products and the oven resource; one dozen iced cookies could be substituted for a dozen sugar cookies in terms of oven capacity and vice versa. Since the other rates of substitution in the product mix example were not one-to-one, the key characteristic of the transportation method was not met by that problem.

Like all linear programming methods, the transportation method is an iterative process. After an initial solution is formulated, the computational procedure provides an effective manner for developing improved solutions until the optimum is reached. The nature and meaning of the steps in this procedure will be demonstrated in the following sample problem.

THE McCLAIN CONSTRUCTION COMPANY

The McClain Company will have four major construction projects under way next month, an unusually high level of activity for the firm. As a consequence, the volume of materials that must be moved from the local supply yard exceeds the capacity of the company's truck fleet. Rather than purchase additional trucks and hire new drivers, the company management has decided to contract with local haulers for as much of the total hauling task as is justified on an economic basis.

The expected hauling requirements, expressed in truckloads, for the construction sites during the next month are as follows:

Site	Requirements (in loads)
No. 1	60
No. 2	90
No. 3	75
No. 4	65

TOTAL 290 loads

Three local trucking firms have submitted bids indicating their price per load from the local supply yard to each site and the maximum number of loads they would be willing to contract for. This information is summarized as follows:

Site	Cost per load Firm A	Firm B	Firm C
No. 1	$6	$3	$6
No. 2	$6	$6	$5
No. 3	$7	$4	$4
No. 4	$7	$5	$3
Maximum Capacity	100 loads	80 loads	70 loads

Expected costs and capacity of the McClain Company's truck fleet for the same period are as follows:

Site	Cost per load McClain Co.
No. 1	$5
No. 2	$3
No. 3	$5
No. 4	$6

Maximum Capacity — 60 loads

Since substantial differences exist in the relative costs of the various assignments that might be made, the McClain Company must now decide which hauling requirements will be assigned to company trucks and which to each of the trucking firms.

5.2 STEP 1: FRAME THE PROBLEM

The technical phases of the problem should be used to develop the basic computation framework or matrix required in the transportation method.

The total hauling capacity (sources) available to the company is the sum of the individual capacities.

Capacity (McClain)	60
+Capacity (Firm A)	+100
+Capacity (Firm B)	+ 80
+ Capacity (Firm C)	+ 70
= TOTAL CAPACITY	= 310 LOADS (5.1)

The total material requirements of the various construction sites (destinations) may also be expressed in equation form.

Requirements (No. 1) + Requirements (No. 2) + Requirements (No. 3) + Requirements (No. 4) = Total Material Requirements

$$60 + 90 + 75 + 65 = 290 \text{ loads} \qquad (5.2)$$

Eqs. (5.1) and (5.2) indicate that the total hauling capacity available exceeds hauling requirements for the period. The transportation method, like the simplex, requires that slack be explicitly recognized. One way of doing this in this particular problem would be to create an artificial or fictitious site requiring 20 loads of hauling capacity.[1] The addition of this slack site to Eq. (5.2) results in the following expression:

$$60 + 90 + 75 + 65 + 20 = 310 \text{ loads} \qquad (5.3)$$

Eqs. (5.1) and (5.3) may now be displayed as the technical or rim requirements of the problem, as shown in Table 5.1.

[1] Occasionally, problems will be encountered where requirements exceed capacity. In such cases, slack would represent unfilled orders.

The technical matrix of a transportation problem serves the same basic purpose as the graphical display of the graphical method and tables of coefficients used in the simplex method. All frame the problem in such a manner as to facilitate the search for better and better solutions.

The 20 cells within Table 5.1 represent the various source-to-destination assignments that are technically feasible. For example, the 100-load capacity of Firm A may be used, in whole or

TABLE 5.1

	Sources of Hauling Capacity				
	Firm				Material Requirements
Site	M	A	B	C	
No. 1					60
No. 2					90
No. 3					75
No. 4					65
Slack					20
Hauling Capacity	60	100	80	70	310

in part, to meet the needs of any of the four sites. A portion of it (up to 20 units) could also be allocated to meet the slack requirement.[2] Any combination of assignments for Firm A would be acceptable as long as the total equaled exactly 100 units. Similarly, the 60-unit requirement of Site No. 1 may be met by any combination of assignments among the various hauling resources as long as the total equals 60.

As in the graphical and simplex methods, the "best" or optimal solution to a transportation problem (a) is feasible, that is, it satisfies all rim requirements; and (b) maximizes or minimizes an appropriate objective function.

The economic data pertinent to the decision are those costs associated with the allocation of a particular source of hauling capacity to each site or destination. For example, each load hauled to Site No. 1 by Firm A will cost \$6; by Firm B, \$3; by Firm C, \$6; and by company trucks, \$5. Considered alone, the lowest cost source for this site would be Firm B at a total cost of \$180 ($60 \times \$3$). Considerations at other sites may, however, call for supplying Site No. 1 from another source if overall cost is to be minimized.

The technical and economic data are summarized in tabular form in Table 5.2. This matrix indicates in explicit form the basic alternatives (cells), the costs associated with each alternative, and the rim requirements. The fact that the problem is framed within the transportation method also indicates, implicitly, that the rates of substitution are all one-to-one.[3]

The final task in framing the problem is to state an explicit objective function. Assuming that the quality of the service provided by the various truck fleets is equal, the minimization of total hauling costs for the month would be a reasonable criterion.[4]

---

[2] An allocation of 20 units of Firm A's capacity to the slack site would mean, in effect, that only 80 units would be contracted for.

[3] The homogeneity assumption in this problem means that one "load" is the same whether it is hauled in company or contractor trucks.

[4] Technically, the assumptions relative to service are not required. If some explicit cost could be assigned to poor service, this cost could be added to the prices within each cell and a pure-cost-minimization criterion adopted.

TABLE 5.2

	Sources of Hauling Capacity				
	Firm				Material Requirements
Site	M	A	B	C	
No. 1	$5	$6	$3	$6	60
No. 2	$3	$6	$6	$5	90
No. 3	$5	$7	$4	$4	75
No. 4	$6	$7	$5	$3	65
Slack	$0	$0	$0	$0	20
Hauling Capacity	60	100	80	70	310

5.3 STEP 2: DEVELOP AN INITIAL SOLUTION

In the transportation method, unlike the simplex, the initial solution need not be the origin solution. The only requirement of an initial solution in the transportation method is that it be technically feasible; that is, it must not violate any of the rim requirements. This means that the amount of subsequent computational work is, in part, a function of the starting position selected.

There are several standard procedures for developing initial solutions. Two appropriate ones for the beginning student are the Northwest Corner Rule and the North to South Row Rule, a simple inspection method. Other more sophisticated methods can be used to advantage once the basic structure of the transportation method has been mastered.

5.31 Inspection Method for Initial Solution. The inspection method used here is a simple one which will be referred to as the North to South Row Rule. This rule operates as follows:

A. Starting with the first or north row, fill the requirements of each row, in order, using the lowest cost assignment available within the limits imposed by previous allocations.

B. After all row requirements have been met, add across each row and down each column to insure that all rim requirements have been met.

The North to South Row Rule will be applied to the McClain problem in the remainder of this section.

Inspection of Table 5.3 shows that the lowest cost capacity for the 60-load requirement at Site No. 1 is Firm B. This

TABLE 5.3

Site	Sources of Hauling Capacity				Material Requirements
	M	A	B	C	
No. 1	$5	$6	$3 / 60	$6	60
—	—	—	—	—	—
Hauling Capacity	60	100	80	70	310

firm has 80 loads available so 60 loads are assigned as shown in cell 1-B. Only 20 loads of Firm B's capacity are now available to other sites.

For Site No. 2 the McClain fleet represents the lowest cost resource but only 60 loads are available (Table 5.4). The additional 30 loads must, therefore, be secured from Firm C, which represents the next lowest cost capacity. Once these assignments have been recorded, the requirements for both Sites No. 1 and No. 2 have been met.

TABLE 5.4

	Sources of Hauling Capacity				
Site	M	A	B	C	Material Requirements (in loads)
No. 1	$5	$6	$3 / 60	$6	60
No. 2	$3 / 60	$6	$6	$5 / 30	90
Hauling Capacity	60	100	80	70	310

Table 5.5 shows two lowest cost sources for Site No. 3 — Firms B and C. However, a portion of their capacities have already been allocated. Also, the McClain fleet has been fully assigned. Therefore, the most economical assignment which can be made at this point is the one shown in Table 5.5.[5]

[5] A feasible alternative would be to secure all 75 loads from Firm A. Such an allocation would not, however, follow our rule of using the lowest cost assignment available.

TABLE 5.5

	Sources of Hauling Capacity				
Site	M	A	B	C	Material Requirements (in loads)
No. 1	$5	$6	$3 / 60	$6	60
No. 2	$3 / 60	$6	$6	$5 / 30	90
No. 3	$5	$7 / 15	$4 / 20	$4 / 40	75
— —	— —	— —	— —	— —	— —
Hauling Capacity	60	100	80	70	310

The initial solution may now be completed by assigning 65 loads of hauling capacity to Site No. 4 and 20 loads to the slack site. Table 5.6 shows that, as a result of previous allocations, it is necessary to select Firm A even though it has the highest cost. Further analysis in later stages will enable adjustments in this and other assignments to be made in the event they are warranted.

TABLE 5.6

	Sources of Hauling Capacity				
Site	M	A	B	C	Material Requirements (in loads)
No. 1	$5	$6	$3 / 60	$6	60
No. 2	$3 / 60	$6	$6	$5 / 30	90
No. 3	$5	$7 / 15	$4 / 20	$4 / 40	75
No. 4	$6	$7 / 65	$5	$3	65
Slack	$0	$0 / 20	$0	$0	20
Hauling Capacity	60	100	80	70	310

Initial Solution: North to South Row Rule

The meaning of the initial solution in Table 5.6 may be interpreted as follows:

(1) Company trucks will haul 60 loads to Site No. 2.

(2) Only 80 loads of the 100 load capacity offered by Firm A will be contracted for. Of the units hired, 15 will haul to Site No. 3 and 65 to Site No. 4.

(3) Sixty loads of Firm B's capacity will be assigned to Site No. 1 and 20 to Site No. 3.

(4) Thirty loads of Firm C's capacity will be assigned to Site No. 2 and 40 to Site No. 3.

This solution is feasible in the sense that none of the rim requirements have been violated. This is the only necessary condition for an initial solution; it need not make much economic sense. The North to South Row Rule for initial solutions did make use of cost data but on a row by row rather than an overall basis.

The cost of this solution (objective function) may be determined by summing the costs for the various sites.

Site No. 1:	$\$3 \times 60$	= \$ 180
Site No. 2:	$\$3 \times 60 + \$5 \times 30$	= 330
Site No. 3:	$\$7 \times 15 + \$4 \times 20 + \$4 \times 40$	= 345
Site No. 4:	$\$7 \times 65$	= 455
Total Cost (Initial Solution)		\$1310

5.32 The Northwest Corner Rule for Initial Solution. There is nothing special about the northwest corner of a matrix. This so-called "rule" is simply a convenient convention which may be stated as follows:

A. Starting at the upper left hand or northwest corner, fill the requirements of each row, in order, from the columns, in order.

B. Check for compliance with rim requirements.

This rule has been applied to the McClain problem in Table 5.7. The 60-load requirement of the first row is met with the capacity of the first (M) column. Move down to the second

TABLE 5.7

Site	Sources of Hauling Capacity M	A	B	C	Material Requirements
No. 1	60				60
No. 2		90			90
No. 3		10	65		75
No. 4			15	50	65
Slack				20	20
Hauling Capacity	60	100	80	70	310

Initial Solution: Northwest Corner Method

row. This requirement is met with 90 units from the second (A) column. The remaining 10 units are applied toward the 75 requirement of the third row. An additional 65 units must be secured from the third (B) column to fill Row 3. The 15 units left in Column B are applied to Row 4. The capacity of Column C is then used to meet the remaining requirement of Row 4 and the slack site row.[6] Adding rows and columns indicates that this is a feasible solution.

Initial solutions based upon the Northwest Corner method can always be recognized by their stair-step appearance. Be-

[6] It is unusual when only one column is needed to fill one row as in Cell 1-M. When this occurs, it is a sign of degeneracy, a condition to be discussed in the next section.

cause the method is concerned exclusively with developing this pattern, it ignores costs. For example, the McClain trucks would have been assigned to Site No. 1 no matter what cost appeared in cell 1-M. The cost data were omitted from the cells of Table 5.7 to illustrate this point.

When properly applied, both the North to South Row inspection method and the Northwest Corner Rule will produce feasible initial solutions. Because the latter ignores costs, more computations are usually required to optimize the problem.[7] Both are acceptable methods, so that the basis for selecting between them is essentially one of personal preference.

5.4 STEP 3: TEST THE SOLUTION FOR DEGENERACY

Degeneracy is a special condition which can arise in any type of linear programming problem. Since it is most likely to occur even in elementary problems when using the transportation method, the beginning student should be able: (a) to recognize the condition, and (b) to devise measures for dealing with it.

Cells within which assignments have been made represent the variables currently in a particular solution. For example, in the initial solution of Table 5.6, cells 1-B, 2-M, and all others with entries are used cells. The unused cells (1-M, 2-A, . . .) are those variables in the problem which are not yet in the solution.

In order to carry out the computation procedure it is necessary that the number of used cells within the matrix conform to the Rim Minus One Rule.

$$\text{Used Cells} = \text{No. of Rows} + \text{No. of Columns} - 1 \qquad (5.4)$$

There are five rows and four columns in the McClain problem. Inspection of Table 5.6 reveals that there are eight used cells. This solution is ready for Step 4. The initial solution of Table 5.7 is degenerate since this matrix contains only seven used cells.

[7] The cost of the initial NW Corner solution is $1395 versus $1310 for the inspection solution. The more "fat" in the initial solution, the more iterations are required.

The measures which must be taken on this matrix will be more readily understood if they are discussed in a later section.[8]

5.5 STEP 4: EVALUATE UNUSED CELLS

The evaluation process of Step 4 tests each unused cell for its effect on the objective function. If an unused cell has a favorable effect (can reduce cost in this case), it is brought into the solution (becomes a used cell). Each cell handled in this fashion must displace a former used cell in order to comply with the Rim Minus One rule. Two alternative procedures for evaluating unused cells will be presented; the Stepping-Stone and MODI methods.

5.51 The Stepping-Stone Method. What would happen if one load were tentatively assigned to cell 2-B as in Table 5.8? Note

TABLE 5.8

	Sources of Hauling Capacity				
Site	M	A	B	C	Material Requirements
No. 1			60		
No. 2	60		1	30	90
No. 3			20		
No. 4					
Slack					
Hauling Capacity			80		

[8] See Section 5.10.

that such an assignment would result in violations of the rim requirements for both Site 2 and Firm B. This means that, if cell 2-B is to be utilized, compensating adjustments must be made in other assignments. For example, if the McClain fleet were to haul 59 rather than 60 loads to Site No. 2, the change would become feasible (59 + 1 + 30 = 90). An alternative would be to decrease the loads destined for Site No. 2 which are carried by the trucks of Firm C (60 + 1 + 29 = 90). To make the proposed change feasible in terms of Firm B, the number of loads to be hauled to Site No. 1 might be decreased to 59 (59 + 1 + 20 = 80), or the loads to Site No. 3 decreased by 1 (60 + 1 + 19 = 80).

For reasons that will become apparent later, suppose that the decision is made to decrease cell 2-C to 29 and cell 3-B to 19 loads. Has the full solution now been restored to a state of technical feasibility? An inspection of Table 5.9 suggests that it has not. Specifically, the change has produced second-order dif-

TABLE 5.9

	Sources of Hauling Capacity				
Site	M	A	B	C	Material Requirements
No. 1			60		60
No. 2	60		1	29	90
No. 3		15	19	41	75
No. 4		65			65
Slack		20			20
Hauling Capacity	60	100	80	70	310

ficulties (side effects) within Row 3 and Column C. Site No. 3 now has only 74 loads assigned, rather than the required 75, and Firm C has been reduced to 69 loads. The only appropriate remedy would be to allocate one additional load to cell 3-C (41 loads). Once this change has been made, the solution is again feasible. Thus, the first step in evaluating unused cells using the Stepping-Stone method is to find the chain of assignment changes (evaluation route) necessary to make the proposal consistent with the rim requirements.

Once these changes have been determined, we determine their effect on the objective function (cost consequences in this problem). The net results of the cell 2-B proposal are summarized:

	B	C
2	\$6 +1 load	\$5 −1 load
3	\$4 −1 load	\$4 +1 load

One load was added to cell 2-B (0 → 1) and to cell 3-C (40 → 41). These changes would add \$10 (\$6 + \$4) to the total hauling cost. At the same time, units were tentatively subtracted from cell 2-C (30 → 29) and from cell 3-B (20 → 19), with a corresponding decrease in hauling cost of \$9 (\$5 + \$4). Thus, the net economic effect of these changes would be to increase the total cost of the solution by \$1 for each load shifted in this manner. Since the objective is to reduce total hauling cost, the introduction of cell 2-B into the solution would not represent an improvement in the assignment mix.

The mechanics of determining evaluation routes is facilitated by following these rules:

(1) Only one unused cell may be evaluated at a time.

(2) Other than the unused cell being evaluated, only used cells may be part of an evaluation route.[9]

(3) There should always be only one unique route for each cell.[10]

Generally the least difficult routes to visualize are those where all adjustments in assignments can be made within four adjacent cells, as for cell 2-B in the sample problem. Routes forming a rectangle, three corners of which are used cells, are also easy to identify. Some routes, however, involve more than four cells and appear to be geometrical equivalents of the "calf path."

An additional illustration should be helpful in developing the meaning of these rules. From Table 5.6, the evaluation of cell 1-C would proceed as follows. The addition of one load to this cell would require that one unit be subtracted from a used cell both in Row 1 and in Column C. The latter adjustment might be made in either cell 2-C or 3-C, while the former can be made only in cell 1-B since this is the only used cell in Row 1. Reduction of cell 1-B by one unit means that one load must now be added to some used cell in Column B. Cell 3-B represents the only possibility. The addition of one unit to cell 3-B would then require subtraction of one unit from some used cell in Row 3, either 3-A or 3-C. Using the latter will complete the cycle in that this will also satisfy the requirement that one unit be deducted from a used cell in Column C. The value of cell 1-C would be +$3 (+ 6 − 3 + 4 − 4). This, of course, is not a favorable move.

---

[9] Early descriptions of this method referred to unused cells as "water" and to used cells as "stones." Thus, only "stones" could be used in evaluating "water" cells; hence the term "Stepping-Stone method" arose.

[10] As long as the number of used cells equals rim-minus-one, this will be true. When two or more feasible routes are found, more assignments have been made than necessary, and the solution can be simplified. Where no route is available, degeneracy is indicated.

Other cells that are relatively easy to evaluate because the evaluation route follows the three filled corners of a rectangle format, are indicated below:

Unused Cell	Route	Economic Effect
3-M	3-M, 3-C, 2-C, 2-M	+$3 per unit
S-C	S-C, S-A, 3-A, 3-C	+$3 per unit
S-B	S-B, S-A, 3-A, 3-B	+$3 per unit
4-B	4-B, 4-A, 3-A, 3-B	+$1 per uni
2-A	2-A, 2-C, 3-C, 3-A	−$2 per un
4-C	4-C, 4-A, 3-A, 3-C	−$1 per u

The evaluation routes for the other cells are s more difficult. The route for cell 1-M, for example 1-M, 1-B, 3-B, 3-C, 2-C, and 2-M, and has an econom +$4. Evaluation of cell S-M involves S-M, 2-M, 2-C, 3-(S-A. Each unit added to this cell will increase the t(the assignment mix by $5. Obviously, this transfe represent a favorable change.

For convenience and ease of analysis it is co note the net economic effect for each unused ce cell, as shown in Table 5.10. Note that only t negative values (2-A and 4-C). These represen to decrease the total cost of the hauling problem.

5.52 The MODI Method for Evaluating Unu Modified Distribution or MODI Method is an

[11] Since this is a cost minimization problem, a positiv represents increased total cost. For profit maximizatior economic data within each cell represent profits rath cell values would represent favorable changes on the m

St

W

TABLE 5.10

Cell Evaluations: First Stage Solution

	Sources of Hauling Capacity				
Site	M	A	B	C	Material Requirements
No. 1	$5 +4	$6 0	$3 60	$6 +3	60
No. 2	$3 60	$6 (−2)	$6 +1	$5 30	90
No. 3	$5 +3	$7 15	$4 20	$4 40	75
No. 4	$6 +4	$7 65	$5 +1	$3 (−1)	65
Slack	$0 +5	$0 20	$0 +3	$0 +3	20
Hauling Capacity	60	100	80	70	310

pping-Stone procedure for evaluating unused cells. It is some-
at more expedient and proceeds as follows:

A. The first row is arbitrarily assigned a zero coefficient.
B. This coefficient together with the cost or profit entries in the used cells are utilized to determine coefficients for all other rows and the columns.
C. Each unused cell is evaluated by subtracting the sum of the corresponding row and column coefficients from the cell entry.

Steps (A) and (B) of the MODI Method for evaluating unused cells are applied in Table 5.11 to the initial solution of Table 5.6. Only the relevant portion of the matrix (cost entries in used cells) is shown. The magnitude of the used cell

TABLE 5.11

Determination of Row and Column Coefficients: MODI Method

R_i ↓	$K_M =$	$K_A =$	$K_B = 3$	$K_C =$	← K_j
$R_1 = 0$			3		
$R_2 =$	3			5	
$R_3 = 1$		7	4	4	
$R_4 =$		7			
$R_S =$		0			

assignments and the cost entries in unused cells are omitted since they are not relevant to these steps.

First, a coefficient of zero is arbitrarily assigned to Row 1.[12]

[12] Actually the arbitrary zero can be assigned to any row or any column. The first row convention will be used here.

Next, the other row and column coefficients are determined using Eq. (5.5).

$$\mathbf{R}_i + \mathbf{K}_j = \mathbf{C}_{ij} \qquad (5.5)$$

where

$\mathbf{R}_i$ = coefficient of the *i*th row
$\mathbf{K}_j$ = coefficient of the *j*th column
$\mathbf{C}_{ij}$ = cost or profit entry in used cell *ij*

For example, the entry in cell 1-B is equal to the sum of the coefficients for Row 1 and Column B ($\mathbf{R}_1 + \mathbf{K}_B = C_{1B}$). Since both $\mathbf{R}_1$ and C_{1B} are known, the equation can be solved for the unknown column coefficient.

$$\mathbf{K}_B = C_{1B} - \mathbf{R}_1 = 3 - 0 = 3$$

Now this column coefficient can be used, together with the cell entry in 3-B, to determine the coefficient of Row 3.

$$\mathbf{R}_3 = C_{3B} - \mathbf{K}_B = 4 - 3 = 1$$

The remaining computations would be as follows:[13]

$$\begin{aligned}
\mathbf{R}_4 &= C_{4A} - \mathbf{K}_A = 7 - 6 = 1 \\
\mathbf{K}_A &= C_{3A} - \mathbf{R}_3 = 7 - 1 = 6 \\
\mathbf{R}_S &= C_{SA} - \mathbf{K}_A = 0 - 6 = -6 \\
\mathbf{K}_C &= C_{3C} - \mathbf{R}_3 = 4 - 1 = 3 \\
\mathbf{R}_2 &= C_{2C} - \mathbf{K}_C = 5 - 3 = 2 \\
\mathbf{K}_M &= C_{2M} - \mathbf{R}_2 = 3 - 2 = 1
\end{aligned}$$

Two important points about these computations should be noted. First, the sequence in which the coefficients are determined is, with minor exceptions, significant. Second, there is only one way in which each coefficient can be computed.

Step (C) of the MODI Method uses the row and column coefficients together with the entries in unused cells as shown in Table 5.12. Used cells are not relevant to this step and are omitted from the table.

[13] The reader should follow these computations using Table 5.11 and enter each coefficient in the table as it is determined.

The evaluation of each unused cell proceeds using Eq. (5.6).

$$E_{ij} = C_{ij} - (\mathbf{R}_i + \mathbf{K}_j) \tag{5.6}$$

where

E_{ij} = Evaluation or value of unused cell *ij*

C_{ij} = Cost or profit entry in cell *ij*

$\mathbf{R}_i$ = Row coefficient for *i*th row

$\mathbf{K}_j$ = Column coefficient for the *j*th column

The computations are straightforward:

$$E_{2A} = C_{2A} - (\mathbf{R}_2 + \mathbf{K}_A) = 6 - (2 + 6) = -2$$
$$E_{1M} = C_{1M} - (\mathbf{R}_1 + \mathbf{K}_M) = 5 - (0 + 1) = 4$$
$$E_{SM} = C_{SM} - (\mathbf{R}_S + \mathbf{K}_M) = 0 - (-6 + 1) = 5$$

TABLE 5.12

Determination of Unused Cell Evaluations: MODI Method

$\mathbf{R}_i$ ↓	**1**	**6**	**3**	**3**	← $\mathbf{K}_j$
0	5 4	6 0		6 3	
2		6 −2	6 1		
1	5 3				
1	6 4		5 1	3 −1	
−6	0 5		0 3	0 3	

Note that these cell evaluations are exactly the same as those obtained by the Stepping-Stone method (see Table 5.10).

The beginner may find it useful to use one as a check on the other. Later, a choice between them can be made on the basis of personal preference.

5.6 STEP 5: DEVELOP REVISED MATRIX

As in the simplex method, there are several criteria that may be used to determine which variable (unused cell) should be brought into the solution at any given stage. A logical criterion for the beginning student is the net effect per unit. In our sample problem, this would lead to the conclusion that cell 2-A is the best alternative since it has the highest potential saving.[14]

The −$2 evaluation of unused cell 2-A indicates that the transfer of one unit into this cell, together with compensating adjustments along the evaluation route, will reduce the total cost of the assignment mix by $2. Since the costs within each cell are linear, it would presumably pay to transfer as many units among these cells as is technically feasible. Consequently, our interests should now be directed toward determining the maximum number of loads that it is possible to transfer along this route.

The status of each cell in the initial matrix (Table 5.10) was as follows:

	A	B	C
2	$6		$5 / 30
3	$7 / 15		$4 / 40

(Cost = $5 × 30 + $7 × 15 + $4 × 40 = $415)

[14] A total effect criterion (cell value × no. of units moved) might also be used. Since the need for reducing computation work is not so great in the transportation as in the simplex method, it makes little difference which criterion is used in elementary problems.

The evaluation for cell 2-A was initiated by tentatively assuming the addition of one unit to that cell. The technical adjustments required to make this change feasible included the addition of one unit to cell 3-C as well as the subtraction of one unit each from cells 2-C and 3-A. The status of these four cells following the transfer of one unit along the evaluation route would be as follows:

	A	B	C
2	\$6 / 1		\$5 / 29
3	\$7 / 14		\$4 / 41

(Cost = \$6 × 1 + \$5 × 29 + \$7 × 14 + \$4 × 41 = \$413)

Note that the cost of these assignments is \$2 less than those of the initial solution. The value of cell 2-A has been saved by the transfer of one unit among these four cells.

If this transfer process were continued, the number of loads within cells 2-A and 3-C would increase while the loads assigned to cells 2-C and 3-A would decrease. Once 15 units have been exchanged in this manner, however, there would be no more units within cell 3-A to add to cell 2-A. Consequently, 15 loads represent the maximum number of units that can be moved along the evaluation route for cell 2-A.

The net decrease in hauling cost represented by this change in the assignment mix would be \$30 (15 units at a saving of $2 each). This saving is also demonstrated by the difference between the initial cost of these cell assignments ($415)

	A	B	C
2	$6 / 15		$5 / 15
3	$7 / 0		$4 / 55

(Cost = $6 × 15 + $5 × 15 + $4 × 55 = $385)

and the cost of the new or revised assignments derived above ($385).

Two general rules may now be stated:

(1) If it is desirable to transfer one unit along a favorable evaluation route, the maximum possible number of units should be moved.

(2) This maximum is determined by that cell within the route having the smallest assignment among those cells from which units are to be subtracted. In the foregoing example, units were to be transferred from both cell 3-A and cell 2-C. The 15 loads within cell 3-A is the smaller assignment and becomes the limiting number for this transfer. Implementation of this change results in a revised matrix (Table 5.13) which represents the second-stage solution.

TABLE 5.13

Second-Stage Solution

	Sources of Hauling Capacity				
Site	M	A	B	C	Material Requirements
No. 1	$5	$6	$3 / 60	$6	60
No. 2	$3 / 60	$6 / 15	$6	$5 / 15	90
No. 3	$5	$7	$4 / 20	$4 / 55	75
No. 4	$6	$7 / 65	$5	$3	65
Slack	$0	$0 / 20	$0	$0	20
Hauling Capacity	60	100	80	70	310

5.7 STEP 6: REPEAT STEPS 3-5 UNTIL AN OPTIMUM SOLUTION IS PROVED BY STEP 4.

The cost of the second-stage solution is $1,280, $30 less than the initial solution. Is it the best possible or optimum solution? Only when Step 4 shows no unused cells with favorable evaluations can we prove that the search for improved solutions may be terminated. Step 6 simply reminds us that linear programming is an iterative process.

5.8 STEPS 3-5 (SECOND STAGE)

All unused cells must be evaluated after each transfer of units has been made, since the evaluation routes for many cells will be changed as a result. Table 5.13 represents the second-stage solution and should be subjected to Steps 3, 4, and 5. Note that cell 2-A is now a used cell. Also, cell 3-A has become an unused cell and is, therefore, no longer eligible as part of: (a) an evaluation route, or (b) the MODI coefficient determination.

The solution is first subjected to the Rim − 1 test for degeneracy. Then the evaluation of unused cells proceeds, using either of the methods demonstrated previously. The MODI coefficients and cell evaluations corresponding to the second-stage solution are shown in Table 5.14.

Examination of the matrix discloses that several evaluation routes and cell values have indeed changed from those appropriate to the initial solution of Table 5.10. The effects on cell 4-C illustrate this point. The route for this cell in Table 5.10 was 4-C, 4-A, 3-A, 3-C. The initial analysis resulted in the withdrawal of all units from cell 3-A, making it an unused cell. At the same time, cell 2-A was changed from an unused to a used cell so that it is now eligible for evaluation routes. The revised route for cell 4-C in Table 5.14 is now 4-C, 4-A, 2-A, 2-C. The new evaluation is −$3 per load as contracted to the $1 saving (-$1 value) found in the initial solution.

Table 5.14 also indicates that cells 4-B and 4-C have negative values; they represent opportunities to reduce cost. Based upon the net-effect-per-unit criterion, cell 4-C should be selected for introduction into the solution. The transfer of units into cell 4-C (and cell 2-A as well) will require that a corresponding number of loads be transferred from cells 4-A and 2-C. The

TABLE 5.14

Cell Evaluations: Second-Stage Solution

Site		M	A	B	C	Material Requirements
		Sources of Hauling Capacity — Firm				
		1	4	3	3	
No. 1	0	$5 +4	$6 +2	$3 60	$6 +3	60
No. 2	2	$3 60	$6 15	$6 +1	$5 15	90
No. 3	1	$5 +3	$7 +2	$4 20	$4 55	75
No. 4	3	$6 +2	$7 65	$5 (−1)	$3 (−3)	65
Slack	−4	$0 +3	$0 20	$0 +1	$0 +1	20
Hauling Capacity		60	100	80	70	310

units within cell 2-C (15) represent the limiting factor in determining the maximum number of units to be exchanged. The expected cost saving that would result from this change would be \$45 (15 × \$3). Implementation of these changes in assignments produces the third-stage solution, as shown in Table 5.15.

TABLE 5.15

Third-Stage Solution

		Sources of Hauling Capacity				
		Firm				
Site		M	A	B	C	Material Requirements
		4	**7**	**3**	**3**	
No. 1	**0**	\$5 1	\$6 (−1)	\$3 60	\$6 3	60
No. 2	**−1**	\$3 60	\$6 30	\$6 4	\$5 3	90
No. 3	**1**	\$5 0	\$7 (−1)	\$4 20	\$4 55	75
No. 4	**0**	\$6 2	\$7 50	\$5 2	\$3 15	65
Slack	**−7**	\$0 3	\$0 20	\$0 4	\$0 4	20
Hauling Capacity		60	100	80	70	310

5.9 STEPS 3-5. (THIRD STAGE)

Examination of Table 5.15 shows that two cells (1-A and 3-A) now have identical negative values. Since the evaluation path of 3-A is the simpler one, suppose that it is selected. Fifty units would be shifted between cells 3-A, 3-C, 4-C, and 4-A. The solution that results (Table 5.16) is shown to be optimal in that there are no cells having a favorable (negative) evaluation.[15]

The total cost of this solution is as follows:

Site No. 1:	$\$3 \times 60$	$= \$180$
Site No. 2:	$\$3 \times 60 + \$6 \times 30$	$= \$360$
Site No. 3:	$\$7 \times 50 + \$4 \times 20 + \$4 \times 5$	$= \$450$
Site No. 4:	$\$3 \times 65$	$= \$195$
Total Cost		$1185

It is interesting to note that this represents a $125 saving over the cost of the initial solution. This cost reduction was achieved by changing the assignments for Sites No. 2, No. 3, and No. 4. The cost of hauling materials to Sites No. 2 and No. 3 was actually increased in the process by $30 and $105 respectively, but this increase was compensated for by a large decrease ($260) in the cost for Site No. 4. The criterion adopted was that of minimizing the total cost rather than minimizing the cost of hauling materials to each individual site. The use of the transportation method of linear programming in the analysis of the problem made the accomplishment of this objective a practical reality.

---

[15] The zero evaluation for cell 1-A means that units could be added to this cell with no change in the value of the objective function. Technically, this means that there is a range of optimal solutions rather than a unique solution for this problem.

TABLE 5.16

Fourth-Stage (Optimal) Solution

Site	M	A	B	C	Material Requirements
	Sources of Hauling Capacity				
No. 1	$5 +2	$6 0	$3 60	$6 +3	60
No. 2	$3 60	$6 30	$6 +3	$5 +2	90
No. 3	$5 +1	$7 50	$4 20	$4 5	75
No. 4	$6 +3	$7 +1	$5 +2	$3 65	65
Slack	$0 +3	$0 20	$0 +3	$0 +3	20
Hauling Capacity	60	100	80	70	310

5.10 METHOD FOR HANDLING DEGENERATE SOLUTIONS

The initial solution developed using the Northwest Corner Rule (Table 5.7) proved to be degenerate; the number of used cells was less than Rim − 1. For this reason, the discussion of Steps 4 and 5 was limited to optimizing the North to

South Row inspection solution. Now that the reader is familiar with the basic computational procedure, the methods for handling degenerate solutions will be demonstrated.

Degeneracy can appear in an initial or any subsequent solution. To restore the number of used cells to Rim − 1, assign some very small number of units ε (epsilon) to one of the unused cells. By definition this number is so small that it has no effect when added to or subtracted from any positive integer. For example, $90 + \varepsilon = 90$ and $10 - \varepsilon = 10$.

The particular unused cell selected for ϵ units is important. In Table 5.17, for example, it is not possible to compute the row and column MODI coefficients unless the ϵ is placed in either

TABLE 5.17

Initial Solution: Northwest Corner Rule
Alternative Adjustments for Degeneracy

R_i ↓	$K_M = 5$	$K_A =$	$K_B =$	$K_C =$	← K_j
$R_1 = 0$	5 / 60				
$R_2 =$		6 / 90			
$R_3 =$		7 / 10	4 / 65		
$R_4 =$			5 / 15	3 / 50	
$R_S =$				0 / 20	

Row 1 or Column M.[16] Normally, the cell having the lowest cost (or highest profit) would be selected (1-B in this case). However, for purposes of illustration, we select cell 1-A and proceed to determine MODI coefficients as shown in Table 5.18.

TABLE 5.18

Initial Solution Modified for Degeneracy

		Sources of Hauling Capacity				
Site		M	A	B	C	Material Requirements
		5	6	8	6	
No. 1	0	$5 / 60	$6 / ε	$3 (−5)	$6 0	60
No. 2	0	$3 −2	$6 / 90	$6 −2	$5 −1	90
No. 3	−4	$5 −4	$7 5	$4 / 75	$4 2	75
No. 4	−3	$6 −4	$7 −4	$5 / 5	$3 / 60	65
Slack	−6	$0 1	$0 / 10	$0 −2	$0 / 10	20
Hauling Capacity		60	100	80	70	310

The ε cell appears (Table 5.18) in the evaluation route of cell 1-B and is the limiting cell for movement of units. In accord-

[16] The ease with which the MODI method signals degeneracy as well as indicates the cell alternatives for ε is an advantage.

ance with the previous definition, we ignore the addition to and subtraction of ε from all cells except 1-A and 1-B. The former becomes an unused cell (since $\varepsilon - \varepsilon = 0$) while the latter becomes the ϵ cell ($0 + \epsilon = \epsilon$) as in Table 5.19. Thus, the only change in this second-stage solution is to move the ε assignment from cell 1-A to 1-B.[17]

TABLE 5.19

Second-Stage Solution: Degeneracy Illustration

		Sources of Hauling Capacity				
Site		M	A	B	C	Material Requirements
		5	1	3	1	
No. 1	0	$5 / 60	$6 / 5	$3 / ε	$6 / 5	60
No. 2	5	$3 / (−7)	$6 / 90	$6 / −2	$5 / −1	90
No. 3	1	$5 / −1	$7 / 5	$4 / 75	$4 / 2	75
No. 4	2	$6 / −1	$7 / 4	$5 / 5	$3 / 60	65
Slack	−1	$0 / −4	$0 / 10	$0 / −2	$0 / 10	20
Hauling Capacity		60	100	80	70	310

[17] This illustrates the fact that cell 1-B should have been selected for ε in the first place. More important, this shows how changes are made when units are to be transferred from the ε cell.

Inspection of the cell evaluations in Table 5.19 indicates that \$7 per load can be saved by transferring 5 units over the route 2-M, 1-M, 1-B, 4-B, 4-C, S-C, S-A, 2-A. While the ϵ cell (1-B) appears in this route, it presents no problems since units are to be added to it, and, by definition, $5 + \epsilon = 5$.

Note that the solution which results from these changes (Table 5.20) has eight used cells with legitimate assignments. Degeneracy can "disappear" in this sense as well as appear at any stage.

TABLE 5.20

Third-Stage Solution: Degeneracy Illustration

		Sources of Hauling Capacity				
Site		M	A	B	C	Material Requirements
		5	**8**	**3**	**8**	
No. 1	**0**	\$5 / 55	\$6 −2	\$3 / 5	\$6 −2	60
No. 2	**−2**	\$3 / 5	\$6 / 85	\$6 5	\$5 −1	90
No. 3	**1**	\$5 −1	\$7 −2	\$4 / 75	\$4 5	75
No. 4	**−5**	\$6 6	\$7 4	\$5 7	\$3 / 65	65
Slack	**−8**	\$0 3	\$0 / 15	\$0 5	\$0 / 5	20
Hauling Capacity		60	100	80	70	310

5.11 SUMMARY

The transportation method, like the graphical, is a special case of the more general simplex method. The key characteristic which permits the simplified format of this method is homogeneity. This means that the rate of substitution between all variables relative to all restrictions is one-to-one.

The computation procedure centers on a matrix that displays all variables in the problem (cells) and the restrictions (rim requirements) for both sources and destinations.

The analysis starts with the development of an initial solution. This may be done using the Northwest Corner Rule or some inspection method such as the North to South Row Rule.

Degeneracy can occur in any linear programming problem but it is especially frequent in the transportation method. The Rim − 1 is a test for degeneracy which must be applied to all solutions. When degeneracy is indicated, an artificial used cell with a very small (ε) assignment is created so that the computation procedure may be continued.

Unused cells may be evaluated by using either the Stepping-Stone or the MODI Method. Those cells having a favorable effect on the objective function are brought into the solution by assigning the maximum possible number of units to them. Each new matrix created in this manner is evaluated until an optimal solution is indicated by the evaluation process for unused cells.

5.12 REVIEW QUESTIONS

1. What is the key characteristic of this method?
2. What is the counterpart of the matrix in the graphical and simplex methods?
3. What criterion must the initial solution to a transportation problem meet?

4. Under what circumstances might the Northwest Corner Rule and the North to South Row Rule produce the same initial solution?

5. What is an evaluation route for an unused cell? Explain how such routes are found.

6. Why do some of the following change from one stage to another?

   a. MODI coefficients.
   b. Evaluation routes.
   c. Evaluations of unused cells.

7. Describe how you would recognize degeneracy using the following:

   a. Rim − 1 Rule.
   b. Evaluation routes.
   c. MODI coefficients.

8. What step must be taken with a degenerate solution?

9. What condition signals that an optimal solution has been reached in the transportation method?

5.13 EXERCISES.

1. The numbers within the cells of the matrix in Table 5.21 represent the expected cost per unit of assigning a series of shop orders (1–4) to each of four work stations (A–D). The number of units required per order and the available capacities of each work station are also shown. The total production cost for the series of orders is to be minimized.
   a. Develop an initial solution using the North to South Row Rule.
   b. Determine the cost of your initial solution.
   c. Carry the problem to an optimal solution using as many matrices as necessary.
   d. Determine the total cost of your optimal solution.
   e. Assuming that maximizing R.O.I. is the highest order economic objective of this firm, justify the use of total cost as the measure of effectiveness in this problem.

TABLE 5.21

	Work Stations				
Order	A	B	C	D	Requirements
No. 1	8¢	5¢	4¢	6¢	65
No. 2	10¢	7¢	5¢	3¢	60
No. 3	6¢	5¢	7¢	4¢	55
No. 4	8¢	9¢	6¢	5¢	30
Capacity	25	65	45	75	210

f. Where is homogeneity a characteristic in this problem? What problems might you encounter in framing this problem from raw machine and order data?

g. Under what circumstances would slack be necessary in a problem of this general type? What would slack represent in each case?

2. Use the Northwest Corner Rule to develop an initial solution to Problem 1.

   a. Will the optimal solution be the same as in Problem 1?

   b. What differences (compared to Problem 1) would you expect in carrying this solution to the optimum?

   c. Illustrate your claims in Problem 2(b) by carrying your initial solution to the optimum.

3. Hoolihan Stores, Inc., a chain organization with four retail stores, is negotiating with four potential suppliers for next month's supply of an item. The maximum number of crates offered by each vendor is as follows: A — 400; B — 650; C — 450; and D — 800.

The buyer for this item has made a careful analysis of vendor prices, transportation charges, store operating costs, and other cost factors. His analysis shows the following expected profit margin per crate:

	Vendor			
Store	A	B	C	D
1	$ .90	$ .60	$ .50	$ .70
2	1.10	.80	.60	.60
3	—	.60	.80	.50
4	.80	1.00	.70	.60

The merchandise carried by Vendor A is not suitable for Store 3; therefore, Vendor A was not asked to bid on this requirement.

a. The expected requirements (in crates) at each store during June are: 1-750; 2-600; 3-550; and 4-300.
   (1) Construct the matrix for this problem.
   (2) Develop an initial solution.
   (3) Carry the problem to an optimal solution and explain the meaning of your final matrix.

b. July's requirements at each store are expected to increase over the June level by 50 units.
   (1) Assuming vendor capacities and expected profit margins remain the same, develop the decision matrix for the July buying decision.
   (2) Develop an optimal solution and explain its meaning.

4. The Reitzson Company operates four manufacturing plants. Shipments are made to four warehouses which fill customer orders from stock. Plant 1 is the company's original manufacturing facility. The family which owns the controlling interest in the firm still resides in the community. Plants 2 and 3 were constructed during the post-war period. Plant 4 is in the first few months of full-scale operation.

a. Each warehouse prepares a sales forecast for each planning period and forwards it to company headquarters at Plant 1. The company president has always prided himself on securing the lowest possible freight charges. As a consequence, all production scheduling has been based upon minimizing total transportation costs for goods shipped between manufacturing plants and company owned warehouses.

The freight charges per unit from each plant to each warehouse are as follows:

		Plant 1	2	3	4
Warehouse	A	$ 9	$ 6	$ 8	$ 7
	B	5	8	9	9
	C	10	11	9	8
	D	7	6	5	8

The expected requirements and maximum plant capacities for the next planning period are as follows:

Warehouse	A:	3100 units	*Plant*	1:	1200 units
	B:	1800		2:	4200
	C:	2000		3:	5000
	D:	4400		4:	2000

(1) In order to minimize transportation charges for the period, what production level should be established for each plant?

b. The production manager has never been very happy about the method used to determine master production schedules.

He suggests that the results of a recent production cost analysis should be incorporated in the decision:

Plant

	1	2	3	4
Standard Cost	$63 (?)	$53	$52	$56
Regular Capacity	1200	3600	4200	2000
Overtime Capacity	—	600	800	—
Overtime Cost	—	$64	$62	—

The production manager explains that the so-called standard cost for Plant 1 is actually about $60 up to 900 units. The poor layout and antiquated equipment result in congestion and inefficiencies at all output figures above 900 units. As a consequence, the last 300 units of capacity actually cost $68 each.

(1) Develop a scheduling matrix which incorporates both transportation and production cost factors.

(2) What output levels should be established for each manufacturing plant during the next planning period?

c. The personnel manager at Plant 1 warns that a strike is imminent. The issues involved are difficult and emotional ones. He suggests that Plant 1 may not be in operation during the next planning period. The president asks that an alternative output schedule be developed based on the assumption that Plant 1 will be closed during the period. The production manager and the Plant 4 manager have an informal agreement that no overtime production will be required this year.

(1) Develop the schedule requested by the president.

5. The Smith Manufacturing Company is scheduling the output of their assembly operations for the next three planning periods. The company assembles two products, A and B. The expected requirements are as follows:

Period 1	*Period 2*	*Period 3*
225 A units	375 A units	450 A units
200 B units	260 B units	300 B units

Regular assembly capacity is 100 hours per period. The following overtime hours have also been authorized: Period 1 — 30 hours; Period 2 — 40 hours; Period 3 — 30 hours. Each A item requires .2 hours and each B item requires .25 hours of assembly time. No backordering is allowed.

Production of both A and B items on overtime results in additional costs of $2.00 per unit. The inventory carrying cost of A items is $1.00 per unit for the first period and $1.20 per unit for the second period following the month of their production. Storage cost for B units is $1.00 per unit for the first period and $1.25 per unit for the second period.

a. Develop the matrix for this problem. (Hint: Use capacities as sources and requirements as destinations.)
b. Use the Northwest Corner Rule for initial solution.
c. Determine the quantities of each product to be produced during each period, if total penalty cost over the 3 periods is to be minimized.
d. Interpret your optimal matrix. What instructions would you give the assembly foreman?
e. If backorders were allowed, how would your matrix differ from the one used above?

SELECTED BIBLIOGRAPHY

Boulding, Kenneth E., and W. Allen Spirey, *Linear Programming and the Theory of the Firm.* New York: The MacMillan Company, 1960.

Bowman, Edward H., and Robert B. Fetter, *Analysis for Production Management* (rev. ed.), Homewood, Illinois: Richard D. Irwin, Inc., 1961.

Charnes, A., W. W. Cooper, and A. Henderson, *An Introduction to Linear Programming.* New York: John Wiley & Sons, Inc., 1953.

Dorfman, Robert, Paul A. Samuelson, and Robert M. Solow, *Linear Programming and Economic Analysis.* New York: McGraw-Hill Book Co., Inc., 1958.

Ferguson, Robert O., and Lauren F. Sargent, *Linear Programming: Fundamentals and Applications.* New York: McGraw-Hill Book Co., Inc., 1958.

Gass, Saul I., *Linear Programming: Methods and Applications.* New York: McGraw-Hill Book Co., Inc., 1958.

Greenwald, Dakota Ulrich, *Linear Programming: An Explanation of the Simplex Algorithm.* New York: The Ronald Press Company, 1957.

Metzger, Robert W., *Elementary Mathematical Programming.* New York: John Wiley & Sons, Inc., 1958.

Reinfeld, Nyles V., and William R. Vogel, *Mathematical Programming.* Englewood Cliffs, N. J.: Prentice-Hall, Inc. 1958.

Vajda, Steven, *Readings in Linear Programming.* New York: John Wiley & Sons, Inc., 1958.